# SUCH A JOURNEY

## Bradford Peace Stories Project
Stories, poems and memories from
Bradford people

Edited by Frances McNeil

Illustrated by Claire Harris

BRADFORD LIBRARIES

Cover and illustrations: Claire Harris

Photographs: Alison Cassidy (pages 17, 38, 63, 66, 98, 104, 106, 108)

Contributors' own photographs

Published by and available from
Bradford Libraries
Central Library
Prince's Way
Bradford
West Yorkshire
BD1 1NN


ISBN 0-907734-42-1

Typeset by MCB University Press in Times New Roman and printed by Dryden-Smith Print Ltd., Oak Mills, Station Road, Clayton, Bradford BD14 6JD.

# DEDICATED TO THE PEOPLE OF BRADFORD

"A cold coming we had of it,
Just the worst time of the year
For a journey, and such a long
journey:
The ways deep and the weather
sharp,
The very dead of winter."

T S Eliot, Journey of the Magi

"...I got the usual telegram in the middle of the night.
Seriously injured. I went down by train with my mother and
all the way bombs were falling. I've never had such a journey in my life."

Doris Hamilton, Helping People

# Acknowledgements

The Peace Stories Project was initiated by the Peace Museum, a project of the Give Peace a Chance Trust (Charity No 327038). It was developed in co-operation with The Commonweal Collection, the Interfaith Education Centre and Touchstone Resource Centre; represented by Carol Rank, Isabelle Guillou, David Fitch and Molly Kenyon, working with Kelvin Ravenscroft, teacher and trainer, encouraged by Dr Sifat Alavi, Zohra Jabeen and a huge network of individuals and organisations.

Volunteers Sera Orzel and Simon Wakeling contributed time and skills. Simon, Molly Kenyon, Isabelle Guillou and Stan Brooksbank did some valuable story collecting.

Bradford & Ilkley Community College staff and students offered support. In particular, input from staff and students at the Art & Design Department enriched the Project. Chantel Burrell, Sarah Jane Grant and Clare Pearson, video makers, recorded at the Federation of Caribbean Elders. Thanks, too, to Bradford Community Broadcasting, Resource Centre and Community Arts Centre.

Bradfordians at schools, colleges, community centres and in their homes were generous with their time and support. You know who you are. Thank you.

The Project, book and exhibition were financed by the Joseph Rowntree Charitable Trust, Bradford Council Cultural Activities Grant, the Barrow Cadbury Trust, Yorkshire & Humberside Arts, the European Regional Development Fund and National & Provincial Building Society. Assistance with publishing from MCB University Press.

Frances McNeil, Peace Stories Project Co-ordinator, was born in Leeds and arrived in Bradford via New York, London, Oxford, York and stops between. Eighteen of her plays have been produced on BBC Radio, Television and in theatres such as Manchester Library Theatre, The Gate, Nottingham Playhouse and Theatr Clwyd. She has written 33 dramatisations and BBC Education scripts. Her short stories have been broadcast and published, with work included in five anthologies. Her play *Tressell*, about the author of *The Ragged Trousered Philanthropists*, is published by Popular Productions.

Frances has recently completed a novel, *Sisters on Bread Street*.

# SUCH A JOURNEY

Stories, poems and memories from Bradford people

*Edited by Frances McNeil*

## CONTENTS

# City of Bradford Metropolitan District Council

## Lord Mayor Councillor Tony Cairns

Lord Mayor's Rooms, City Hall, Bradford, West Yorkshire BD1 1HY

# FOREWORD

This year is proving very special. Not only is Bradford celebrating its centenary, but Bradfordians have created a unique and lasting gift for each other - this book. People of all ages and backgrounds have contributed memories, stories and poems. Some stories touch on events of major international significance, such as the Second World War, the Partition of India and the expulsion of Asian people from Uganda. Others have a more domestic focus - exploring love and loss; friendship and struggle. Yet all these pieces are astonishingly vivid and possess a timeless quality. In William Blake's words, 'Here is the world in a grain of sand'.

Some contributors are still at school or college and express their hopes for the future and their environmental concerns. Other contributors work for groups and organisations that promote justice, peace and mutual understanding. They do so in the most practical ways that meet people's social and spiritual needs. Some are now retired and have time to look back and reflect. There is a surfeit of talent here that will enlighten, move and inspire. We must listen to each other if we are to create the peaceful and harmonious future we all desire.

*Tony Cairns*

The Lord Mayor of Bradford 1997-98
Councillor Tony Cairns
July, 1997

# INTRODUCTION

"Don't stand too close to other children or you'll catch their dreams," a friend's mother once warned her as she set off for a children's party. Years later my friend realised that she had misheard and had been warned not against catching dreams, but germs.

Starting out on this collection last July, I was in need of such a warning – not against germs but against dreams. Dreams, memories and inspiration tumble and flow through Bradford with enough energy to power the district. I tried not to mishear as I went here and there, sometimes with a tape recorder, sometimes a shorthand pad. Other work came in written form – individual pieces or whole biographies, published and unpublished. My great regret is that it is not possible to include every piece that I liked and admired.

For a long time the favourite self-image for Bradford was as a place where everyone got on well despite their differences. The truth is that we largely ignore each other and get on with our lives until something goes wrong.

I hope this book will be a good read and that it will help in some small way towards creating greater mutual understanding and recognition of the things that unite us, as well as respect for differences. There is a lot of segregation and separation in Bradford, but what emerges again and again is the shared sense of struggle. So many people have struggled through painful and adverse experiences and have, mainly, courageously, come through. That in itself is a peace story.

Frances McNeil
July 1997

---

**EDITORIAL HEALTH WARNING**

Turning these pages puts you seriously at risk of catching dreams

---

11

FAMILIES

# THE HUMAN CHAIN

## *Maria Lelzczyszyn*

We five children lived with our mother in Stryj, a small town in the Ukraine. Father died when I was very young. My mother had a dog that she loved. The river used to flood, sometimes to here – ankles – sometimes to here – chest.

My mother loved that dog and when it was caught in the swollen river she went to help it. The fierce flood took my mother, and we children saw that she was drowning. All five of us formed a chain, holding hands, and we caught hold of my mother and saved her. She died here in Bradford. So did my husband who was diabetic. I have three children.

# COFFEE AND CREAM

## Michelle Etoria

I hated my sister! Especially on the day she punched me in the mouth and made my lip swell up like a balloon. She looked horrified when she saw the blood trickle onto Mum's carpet.

I bet you're scared now, I thought. Mum's going to kill you. I wanted to kill her myself but she was twice my weight and older.

Okay, so I was the youngest and yes, I was spoilt rotten. Now that I'm older I can see why my sister hated me.

Our mum had three children all to different fathers – men, whatever you call them. Mum would often explain to people, "I have a child to a West Indian, a Pakistani and a Hungarian". She'd finish off by saying in a very prideful voice, "At least they can't say I'm not Miss International".

Reflecting back over my childhood I can remember Mum playing her reggae records at full volume so our street had no choice but to share the beat. Mum's concert took place every Sunday morning. On the corner of our street is a Ukrainian Church and God knows what they must have thought of us. They never seemed hassled by Mum's reggae beat on their way to church. In fact they always smiled and said good morning.

But back to the day of the balloon lip. Mum had returned from work. She had a few jobs in those days, working at night at the biscuit factory and as a cleaner through the day. I remember we couldn't talk about Mum's jobs to anyone – especially not to the man who came to see us from the Department of Health and Social Security that day. The same day I got punched in the mouth by my big sister.

My sister had legged it before Mum got back from work which left Mum and my big swollen lip to face the man from You Know Where. I remember the man looking around our house and asking Mum questions. They couldn't have been nice questions because Mum told him to p.off and go back to where he came from.

Then I had to listen to Mum go on about how the man had looked into her knicker drawer. She stopped going on about him when she'd finally managed to stick her false eye lashes on and go out with Auntie June dancing. Which left me stuck with fisticuffs yet again. That night my sister resorted to using her mouth to attack me, due to the coat hanger Mum had slapped around her legs earlier on.

Two decades on and I am pleased to say there is peace between my sister and me. We do not fight any more and I do not hate her. We have grown to love and respect each other. I never thought I'd love my sister as much as I do now. I don't see my sister as much as I'd like to, due to our hectic and demanding life styles. I'm a volunteer youth counsellor and I'm hoping to go into counselling as a full time career. My sister's kept busy with her family.

However, when we do find some time to spend together it's very special. Mum, the old time Lovers Rock chick, is now a hard core follower of Islam. The other day we were drinking tea and eating toast when out of the blue Mum said, "Look at my two beautiful daughters – Coffee and Cream".

Michelle Gizella Etoria with her mother and sister, Ayusha Maryam Khan and Carol Dawn Etoria-Singh

# LITTLE BABY SOFT AND NEW
## This is what I want for you …

*Sonyah Ayub*
Grange Road First School

A world with peace.
A world with love.
A world with fruit.
A world with colleges.
A world with shoes.
A world with socks.
A world with milk.
A world with no kidnapping.
A world with schools.
A world with drink.
A world with clothes.
A world with a family.

# HELPING PEOPLE

## *Doris Hamilton*

My father, James Harrison, was the first Lord Mayor of Bradford who refused to wear a top hat. He was a revolutionary, like me. He was Lord Mayor in 1942, when Winston Churchill visited Bradford. When my dad died, in 1956, a bus driver stopped his bus and got out and came to speak to me. "The world's a better place for your father being in it", he said. That's what's important, helping people. Dad knew what it was like to be poor because they had no money. His dad died and he was sent to the workhouse, where St. Luke's is now. He was born in 1880, in Cabinet Street. He had no education. He was a twin and his twin died and his mam said he had the brains of both of them. He could recite Shakespeare and quote the Bible, though he wasn't religious. He could tell the tale and was a very good speaker. He was Councillor for what was called North Ward where poor folk lived up Bolton Road. Eventually he was councillor for Bradford Moor. Dad was in the Labour Party and in the Dyers and Bleachers' Union. We used to argue cats and dogs. One thing we were agreed on and that was our opposition to war. "They should take the old uns like me and put us at the front", my dad said.

My mother, Charlotte, was a lovely lady and very kind. She was taken ill in 1942 and so I came back from Oxford where I was working. She lived to be a hundred and during the last four years of her life I didn't leave the house. The lady who lived next door did the shopping and the collector came for the rent.

Mostly I did part-time jobs, though there was a time when I was a full-time Welfare Officer, in 1945, and I loved that because I was able to help people who had war injuries, and former prisoners of war. I was always on their side. It was complicated work and there was a "code" you had to follow. I had to leave to look after my mum. I have a letter from the Minister of Health thanking me for my work and I used it as a reference when I applied to do a few hours in the Tax Office.

I was born 2nd August 1910 in Bradford and we lived on Maperton Road by Barkerend School until 1926. That was the year I joined the Independent Labour Party. A friend told me that they went on good walks, that was why I joined. Some joined for the dancing. It was a lively organisation. We'd meet in

Jowett Hall (now Bradford Civic Theatre) named after Fred Willie Jowett, MP, one of the first people to argue for free school meals for poor children. We have a lot to be proud of in Bradford. The first public wash house was up Leeds Road. Bradford was the first place in the country to have a municipal hospital. Dad was on the old Board of Guardians and held many a meeting in our back yard. Poor people came with children in their arms and no food.

I went to all the ILP conferences and I met a lot of sincere people. Some had been in concentration camps. Others fought on the Republican side in the Spanish Civil War, opposing the Fascists. Lilo Linke, a refugee, came and stayed a few days. Last I heard she'd written a book called Black Cat Across My Path. She was a typical German girl, bright blue top, navy skirt, red scarf. I met Jimmy Maxton, MP, Jimmy McGovern and Vic Feather who became General Secretary of the Trades Union Congress. There were some good speakers but the best, the most promising and the most intelligent of them all was Tom Hamilton. He was one for helping people, like me. He spoke all over Scotland and was tipped as a future foreign secretary. We married in 1936.

Doris Hamilton with her parents and the comedian, Ted Ray

Although I was nervous, I spoke at meetings, too, well-attended public meetings in Peel Park. I spoke against the war. You get into war and you don't know you're in it until it's all too late.

Tom and I went to live in Scotland but on the outbreak of the Second World War, in 1939, we came back to Bradford because it was clear he'd be conscripted and he didn't think it fair on me to be in Scotland away from my relations. He was in the York & Lancashire Regiment but while everyone else was sent to Otley for training, he was sent to Paisley near Glasgow. He got out of the religious part. No church for him.

Tom was a lance sergeant and it was while he was on manoeuvres in Colchester that I got the usual telegram in the middle of the night. Seriously injured. I went down by train with my mother and all the way bombs were falling. I've never had such a journey in my life. I knew he was dead before I got there. You hear about people having premonitions and stuff, and I knew. I met someone on the station but I said, "I know it's hopeless. My husband's dead". And he was.

There was an inquest, but how could it be explained? You can't argue with them. I didn't even get his belongings, that's the thing that hurts - his poetry, his speeches. I never got it. I went to see Jimmy Maxton at the House of Commons but I didn't get Tom's stuff. They destroyed everything.

There are three war widows in my family from the Second World War and three from the First World War. One uncle had a plate in his head, one had a tropical disease. Tom's brother was a prisoner of war in Japan, but he bore no malice. He'd met a Japanese lad who was very good to him while he was a prisoner. There's good and bad in every country.

Questions run through my mind. What am I doing here in a residential home? What happened to all those people I knew? I have glaucoma now so I can't read and only someone who loves to read knows what that means. I listen to the television and I shout at it. It's all bad news. So many people are selfish now, just interested in getting their money. I came into this home because they said, "What if you fall?" Well I'm here and I have fallen. I fell over there by the window. I got up again.

Sometimes I remember all those good people from the Independent Labour Party and all the hopes we had to make the world better. Where have they all gone?

# SEVEN SISTERS AND TWO BROTHERS

*Wanda Rolbiecka*

There were nine children in our family. Every year a child, and times were very difficult with nothing to eat. I was born on 10 January 1906 and so remember the First World War as well as the Second. My young days were very bad. My older sister died and I am the second. My father was an organist and played in the church and an orchestra, and he was a singer. Bronislawa, my eldest sister who died in 1941, she had a wonderful voice. My brother in Poland, Walerjan, he plays the organ too. He is 82.

In 1944 the Germans took me from Warsaw in Poland to Germany, just in what I stood up in. It is painful to think about even now. I am working in the factory making munitions, living in barracks. After the war the British asked me do I want to work in England, and I say yes and come here.

I work in the mill and speak English okay but now my English I forget. My husband was in Polish army. He died in 1966. I have been alone a long time. I come every week to the Polish Centre. For me it is very good to speak Polish. It gets hard when you are old.

Five years ago four of us sisters were together. Stanislawa came from America, Ewelina from Australia and Jadwiga from Poland. That was a good time, all together, visiting.

# THE BOY WHO NEVER LAUGHED OR CRIED

## Brenda Thomson

"Well then" Stephen asked, "Are you going to join?"

We had been visiting Peter in the Children's Home for about three months.

We had first heard about Peter through an advertisement in the Telegraph & Argus:

> Boy, aged six, been in residential care for most of his life,
> would like a Mummy and Daddy without children to look after
> him all the time, and a bicycle.

My gut reaction to this was that for a child whose only knowledge of family life was the Children's Home, a mother and father to himself would be smothering. What he needed was a family, but with love and security. So we volunteered, our five children, three of them adopted and from multi-racial backgrounds, various cats, a rabbit, gerbils, and bikes of all sizes.

And so he joined. Peter had been left behind in St. Luke's hospital at birth, child of shame of an East African Sikh family. He was a small, sad child, with scratches down his cheeks from the bullying he suffered in the Home. They told us he never laughed and never cried. We discovered that he had a white hot temper and could swear with competence. He was well behind the other children in his school work and his emotional development seemed almost non existent. He didn't laugh. He didn't cry. His physical appearance was quaint, with a shock of wiry black hair, ears that stuck out like jug handles and a jutting chin. He spoke very little, but he quickly learned to ride a bicycle and to start to save for a new one of his own. He watched the other children and he listened.

The family absorbed Peter with little fuss - another child to join in the games, to squabble with, to feed and clothe and to love. Some months later I found a group of them sitting on the landing at the top of the stairs around an old record player, with one of their favourite records on the turntable, a Spinners' version of "The ink is black". They were singing along with gusto, except for Peter. He had tears streaming down his cheek as he listened:

"The child is black, the child is white;
The whole world looks upon the sight.
What a beautiful sight."

I don't know what had triggered it exactly, but it was indeed "a beautiful sight". Laughter came soon afterwards.

School was a struggle for Peter. His late start, his physical appearance, a speech impediment, his immaturity in relationships were all weighted against him. Hard pressed teachers in mainstream school were unable to give him the support that he needed. His brother and sisters stood up for him, fiercely protective when they were mocked for having a "boggy-woggy" brother. Through the misfortune of coincidence, the child who had bullied him in the Children's Home came from a local family and made regular home visits. He frequently called for Peter to play out, so he too was invited into the garden. With "the family" to contend with he found his place. It was never a happy relationship from Peter's perspective and often led to rage but no more bullying.

In time we managed to persuade Bradford Education that Peter could be better served in a school for children with special learning needs. He was moved to an all boys school and was very happy there. He seemed to be able to settle in with confidence and sort out his gender identity in that environment. His school work began to progress too, though he was always to be a slow learner. He was able to indulge his love for football, always aspiring to get into "the first squad" but never quite making it.

Woodwork seemed to be an important part of the curriculum. Most weeks he would bring home some offering or other, carefully cut out of old desk wood and lovingly sand papered or painted - a car, a rocket, an engine, a gun, a rifle, a cannon, a catapult. In some exasperation I said to him, "Doesn't your teacher know that I'm a pacifist!" The next time he brought home a carefully sanded dove on a stand, a warm, golden token of affection, proudly offered, that still sits on the kitchen dresser.

One day he decided to tidy out his bedroom. The wooden cars, rocket, guns, catapult were consigned to the firewood box in the cellar. Out too went his toy soldiers and many of the other trappings of boyhood. He said: "I'm too old for these now I'm thirteen. Can we give them away?" He kept his stamp album, Subbuteo football game and a pile of football memorabilia from his favourite club, Ipswich Town.

It was one of those busy mornings, two weeks later. I was sorting the washing when he called out to me, "Can I wear my best shirt today?" Well, I thought, he might as well wear it before he grows out of it. Today was the day he had been selected for the football squad to play a match against another Special School. We went through the early morning scrabble of breakfast, school bags and lost homework. He was the first to leave to catch the bus to school. He called "Bye", and he was off with a slam of the door.

A phone call came at about four o'clock in the afternoon, from a Chemist's on Peter's route home from school. There had been an accident. Would I go to the Bradford Royal Infirmary as soon as possible. Not to worry but I was needed. My brain went into rapid scan. The Infirmary was a fifteen minutes walk away – I could get there more quickly on my motor scooter, but perhaps if Peter was unable to walk I would need to bring him home in a taxi; walking would be better; what about the other children about to return from school; leave a note; tell them not to worry, it would be alright.

It was a glorious November day, with the evening sun shining softly on the fading trees. The wind was sweeping the fallen leaves into the rustling piles of red and gold. I scrunched through the autumn leaves in my boots.

When I got to the hospital they were very gentle. They showed me into a side ward, and all I could see was his red football socks sticking out from under the sheet. His sweet face was very peaceful, a bit of a bruise on his chin. His hair stuck up every which way. He had just collapsed, running home from school. No warning. He was dead on arrival ... a post mortem.

I can't remember why I couldn't get hold of my husband Keith. But I do remember that I rang home and Stephen was in. I told him the news over the phone and asked him to come for me. Stephen, the tall, black fifteen year old who was giving me such a hard time, came up to the hospital and comforted me like the man he really was and we went home together.

A row of classmates who attended his funeral had chosen Peter's favourite school hymn for us to sing, "One step at a time, with Jesus". They visibly cheered as we left the church to the sound of the signature tune for "Match of the Day". Peter had played in the school first team match that day. It was years later, however, that I learnt from a teacher at the other school that he had played for their side. "Oh, didn't you know? He wasn't needed in his team," he said. "The other squad was short of a player and Peter volunteered". The post mortem found that Peter had a congenital heart defect, of a kind quite common in the local Punjabi community. He had literally played his heart out at football – for the other side!

Unbeknown to us his death could have happened at any time but we had the joy of Peter in the family for over six years. And how he had grown. He had had an evening paper round to supplement his pocket money and just managed to buy a new bike. He was well known by the local elderly folk as ever ready

25

with a cheery word when he delivered the Telegraph & Argus. He really was the Boy Scout who helped old ladies over the road, whether they wanted to go or not. The loving stories they told us after he had gone.

There was the time he found a small kitten wandering in the street as he was on his rounds. He decided that it needed a home. So he took it to one elderly lady because he said he thought she was lonely and could do with a friend. Goodness only knows whether the kitten was ever returned to its original home. One senior citizen offered him a Christmas tip, only to have it politely returned because, he said, he thought the man was poorer than him and needed the money more.

What a success Peter had made of his short life, from so unpromising a beginning. The boy who never laughed or cried gave so much love.

# PEACE
# AND WAR

# FOR PATRIOT, READ SCOUNDREL

## Robert Swindells

31st August 1940. A warm night. Britain has been at war for almost a year but no bombs have fallen on Bradford. Unbeknown to its sleeping citizens, this is about to change. The siren's wail, rising and falling, sounds across the city. The people wake, tumble from their beds, head for the shelters. I am seventeen months old. My father and grandmother carry me to the Anderson shelter at the bottom of the garden. They lay me in a clothes basket on the earthen floor and I fall asleep. I know nothing of war.

Outside, searchlights probe the sky. There is gunfire, and the sounds of aeroplane engines. Bombs start to fall. An orange glow tells of something, somewhere on fire. On the other side of the city my mother lies in the maternity ward of St Luke's Hospital with my newborn brother, Donald. Concerned for their safety and careless of his own, my father leaves the shelter and sets out to walk there.

The raid lasts several hours. It is not a heavy raid as such things go but fires are started, buildings are destroyed. Over a hundred people are wounded. I sleep through it all. Grandma watches over me. She doesn't know what has happened to my mother and father. When the all clear sounds she carries me back to the house and tucks me into my cot. She can't rest. She brews a pot of tea and waits.

In the morning my father comes home. Mother and baby are safe. He has spent the night with them in the hospital corridor. All the beds are wheeled into corridors in case blast causes glass to fly in the wards.

Time passes. In 1958 I am serving with the Royal Air Force at Mönchen-Gladbach in Germany. At Christmas most of my friends get home leave, but I have guard duty. The parents of my friend Gisela Muller invite me to spend Christmas Day with them in their home. The house is full of family and everybody is kind to me. In the evening we sit around the fire with warming drinks, talking. Because I have little German they speak English. Herr Muller asks me, "Where in England do you live?" I tell him "Bradford," and he grins. "I flew sometimes over Bradford," he says, "on my way to bomb Manchester and Liverpool." I tell my clothes basket story. Everybody smiles, nods. Some have stories, not dissimilar, of their own.

I look around at this family, enjoying Christmas in much the same way as my own family enjoys it, and I wonder what it is that drives us at intervals to slaughter one another. Why would Herr Muller, who smiles at me now over the rim of his glass, have killed me in 1940? Why would my Uncle Arthur, who flew Lancasters and was fond of children, have killed Gisela?

Now, forty years on, one thing is clear to me. It is that if ordinary people were not lied to about the reasons for war; if we were told the real reasons, none of us would fight. Who in their right mind would march off to die for access to raw materials, markets, spheres of influence, or to boost the popularity of some stay-at-home leader? A wiser man than I once said, "Patriotism is the last refuge of scoundrels". Quite so, and if the scoundrels told the truth, there'd be no more war.

# DACHAU

*John Sugden*

At the railhead
A mile from town,
Barbed-wire-fenced dog runs,
Watch towers and floodlights.
The iron gates of hell,
Inscribed Arbeit Macht Frei.

Safe to enter decades later.
A notice instructs me
To show respect,
Bring no literature,
To dress properly.
Not to write on walls
But to reflect on the victims
Of industrialised genocide.
Amongst modern sculptures,
Pierced and twisted nature,
Inarticulate memorials
In the names of nations,
God's disputatious legions,
In the camp of Dachau
Museum of death.

Treading clean, crisp, gravel paths
Not one weed shows its head,
No non-Aryan vegetative strain.

In the pine-built barracks
No blood, no bones, no fleas, no lice,
No guts, no shit, no stink, no sweat.
Three tiers of beds or shelves
Where once were lain two thousand
In each of thirty blocks.
Stripped of possessions,
Torn from kin and loved ones.
Denied identity, future, past,
Subject of experiment
Under SS discipline
Hung for an hour
From wrists tied behind -
The penalty for dirtiness
In the Nazi cesspool.
Two from three worked to death.
Entered in accounts
At values of gold, rags, hair and bone.
Arbeit Macht Frei.

Outside it rains,
Misting the nearby town.
Obscuring observers, perpetrators.
And from behind me
The sound of a child running,
Spraying bullets from Daddy's umbrella,
Which is repossessed
For more peaceful purpose.
And there at the gate
Stands a solitary,
Bearded, black-clad Jew,
As if from that earth
The first of Spring.

# THEY CAME WITH LORRIES

## Anna Husak

I was taken to Germany from my home in Ukraine two days before my six-teenth birthday, July 1942, just in what I stood up in. I was the eldest of seven children and my youngest brother was eight months old so they were still there. I didn't see them for fifty years after I was taken. Twenty years ago we tried to bring my mother and sister here but the Ukrainian authorities said No. So I never saw my mother again. My sister has been here three times. I am disabled now and I lost my husband three years ago.

It was one o'clock in the afternoon when they came with lorries and loaded all us young people in. Some people ran away. I don't know why I didn't run. I was with a German family on a farm and I couldn't complain. I was well fed and treated though I got homesick. They were friendly to me. Good. In every country there are good and bad people. I had only two or three hours Sunday afternoons to see my friends, young Ukrainian people, some worked in the factory.

# IN BARI

## from The Bird is on the Wing

### *Moyra Platts, M.B.E.*

During the Second World War, I served with the Auxiliary Territorial Army Expeditionary Forces. In December, 1943, we embarked for Italy on the Maloja, a British India liner in service as a troop ship. After a brief spell in Naples, I was posted to Bari, a harbour town in the Southeast.

Italy had joined with the Allies against Germany, but fighting was still going on in the North of Italy. In the South, Italians in the liberated territories took reprisals against collaborators and quislings. A vicious campaign was directed against women suspected of fraternizing with the hated Tedeschi (German soldiers). Victims were relentlessly hunted and punished by having their heads completely shaved. The hair took months to grow again, so it meant a long sentence of misery and humiliation.

In Bari, gangs of fanatical students handled the women very roughly. Those who tried to resist were horribly mutilated; and several received fatal injuries. Working in the office one hot summer night, I heard a familiar commotion in the distance. Then, with sudden horror, I knew that the mob was heading straight in my direction. The only shoes the Italians could get were roughly made sandals whose wooden soles made a distinctive slapping noise – this unmistakeable clatter now passed the lodge and stopped outside the gate. There was a wild hammering and desperate cries for help. Without thinking of the consequences, I ran out, pulled a frenzied girl through the door and bolted it again. There was no time to reach the safety of the flats. I flicked off the lights and we crouched under the office table. The girl's pursuers wrenched at the gate and tried to climb the lodge. Their torch beam probed the corners but did not discover our hiding place. The girl shook convulsively, my own heart thumped sickeningly as I realized that if the mob did break in, I could not even claim immunity as a British Service woman - because of the heat I'd changed into shirt and shorts! The mob would undoubtedly attack me too ... I should put up no resistance ... anything to escape a worse fate.

Miraculously, the bolt on the little door held, attempts to climb the walls, or wrench the bars from the windows failed and after a seeming eternity the mob withdrew to continue the hunt elsewhere. When it was quiet, I took the girl up to the flats and roused a sergeant. It was difficult to believe that the noise had not disturbed the whole company, but most of our windows faced another way.

The girl was almost incoherent, and our knowledge of Italian too limited to understand her story. As soon as it was daylight she insisted on going home. We never saw her again. I hope she escaped retribution; she was scarcely more than fifteen, and whatever her crime or indiscretion, she had already paid most

Moyra Platts

dearly in the terror of that night. People can never anticipate how they will react in an emergency; I had been involved in all sorts of minor adventures, but this was by far the most frightening experience. And my actions were prompted not by any pre-conceived plan or by courage, but purely on impulse. Had I not intervened, the girl might have been murdered outside the gates.

# NOVO LJUMOVIC'S WAR STORY

## Stan Brooksbank

Novo and I are members of West Park Veterans' Bowling Club. His life has been eventful and his war time experiences perilous. Survival frequently depended on his own resourcefulness and quick thinking as well as the kindness of strangers.

At the outbreak of the Second World War in 1939, Novo was a 17 year old air force cadet who had left his home in Podgorica, Montenegro for Nish in Eastern Serbia where he took an aeronautics course.

When Novo was 19, Yugoslavia was surrounded by Axis (German and Italian) forces and the government signed a pact with Hitler, agreeing to supply goods to Germany as long as the country was not invaded. The Serbs did not trust the Germans but were pressured into signing the pact by Croatians and Slovenians. In return, Germans agreed not to invade Yugoslavia. On 27th March, 1941, two days after the pact was signed, the government was overthrown and Prince Regent Paul imprisoned. On 6th April at 2 a.m., Hitler declared war on Yugoslavia. King Peter escaped to Greece, then Egypt and finally London. Novo was in Belgrade when armistice was declared on 17th April, 1941.

He went home to Montenegro and then on to Split. With three friendly Croats, he was taken prisoner by pro-Nazi Croats. However, when his captors realised that Novo's uncle was a teacher they admired, they released him and he was advised to change his name to Lubisch, a Croatian name.

Novo and his three companions continued on to Bugajno where they were arrested and marched to the Town Hall. Two agreed to join the Croat forces. There was a disturbance when Germans arrived and someone threw hand grenades at a statue. In the confusion that followed, Novo and Mate Kuzmanich escaped and caught a bus back to Split the following morning. From Split, Mate planned to go to an island where he had relations. Years later, Novo discovered that Mate had escaped with his wife and two children to Egypt and then to Australia in a British submarine. Novo had suspected that Mate was a British agent, and this would explain the help that he received from the British.

Split was occupied by Italians who arrested Novo and imprisoned him in a camp in Bergamo for a year and then in a camp in Central Italy. In September, 1943 Italy surrendered and once again taking a chance Novo fled from the camp into the mountains. He received help from sympathetic peasants who fed him.

In his attempt to get to the British lines, he came to a large house where he was allowed to sleep in the stable, given decent clothes and directed to a little shack where there were six others on the run. As the one who could speak Italian, Novo volunteered to find food. Once again he was lucky. At a farm house a woman gave him beans, bread and potatoes.

The little band's luck ran out when one day Germans came to the shack at 2.00 a.m. with machine guns and grenades and captured them. Novo was badly treated. When he told them he was a Yugoslav, a soldier put a gun to his head and told him there was no such place. Before the soldier pulled the trigger, Novo had the presence of mind to say, in German, "I am a prisoner of war". His quick thinking saved his life.

Novo Ljumovic and Stan Brooksbank

He was taken to Fiuggi, near Cassino and again interrogated. He was then sent to a prisoner of war camp near Rome. The British there advised him to escape, put him in a wheel barrow and covered him. He was discovered, badly beaten, and interrogated at Terni.

The Germans' plan was to ship Novo and other prisoners to Germany but on the eve of their departure a British bombing raid disrupted operations. In the darkness and confusion, Novo and a friend from Yugoslavia, poorly clad and without shoes, made their escape.

They climbed a high fence with a big drop on the other side. Novo's friend broke his arm and they found themselves by a minefield. A kindly Italian led them away from the mined area and Novo made a sling for his friend's arm. After some distance they came to a forestry house. A man with a gun challenged them but when he heard they were trying to escape he gave them clothes and shoes and told them which path to follow.

Soon they were halted by two S.S. men. Novo had the presence of mind to swear in Italian about the British bombing, and the S.S. men let them continue.

They reached four houses and were surprised to see a lady in a nightie holding and stroking a pig. Novo asked her for a doctor for his friend and was delighted to find that her husband was a doctor. He was anti-Mussolini and had been imprisoned for ten years. Now he was in hiding. The doctor treated them to bread, cheese, pasta and a splint for the friend's arm. For fourteen days Novo and his friend stayed with the couple. During this time there was a dangerous moment when four Germans banged on the door. The doctor welcomed them.

"Have some wine and pasta," he said.

The Germans got very drunk and left their machine guns behind. The doctor called out to them to take them. The next day, Novo saw a spitfire shot down.

Some Italians came to the doctor and said, "The English have arrived in the village".

This was the good news Novo had been waiting for. Free at last! They went back into the town with the doctor and his wife, to their old house. The house was in ruins. The Germans had destroyed everything but a grand piano which was made in Berlin.

In the ruined house, the doctor's wife played and sang for them. She was a former opera singer and the niece of General Bodeglio who signed the Peace Treaty.

Novo was sent to Naples and Taranto. There he joined the Balkan Operational Air Force – a branch of the Royal Air Force composed of airmen of many nationalities – servicing planes. When the war finally ended, he was sent to Northern Italy and later to Hamburg. There was pressure on Yugoslavs to return home and join Marshall Tito, but as an anti-Communist Novo preferred to join the British Air Force.

Novo met up with his old friend Vic Stefanovic in Taranto and again in Foggia and Naples. Vic was given a duty to guard German prisoners in Treviso. When they left the army, Novo and Vic came to Bradford and they lived in Ash Grove. Novo married Kathleen Richardson from Brighouse in 1953. His friend Vic died in a car accident in June 1996.

# I CRY, I FEEL ANGRY

## *Anna Wloch*

I was 13 years old when the Germans took me to work on a farm in Germany, without pay. I was the only daughter at home. My father died, I don't know when. My mother was killed by Russians. I got married when I was 17, to Basil Wloch. Basil's dad died when he was nine months old and his mother died when they came to England. He has one brother and two sisters, one came to England and was treated for cancer. Now she is dead.

We brought up six children and have ten grandchildren. We didn't have it easy as we had nothing at first, no spoon, no knife. We bought a cottage. The children got a good education. Now we're doing well.

I have been five times to Ukraine to visit family and every time I go I cry. I feel angry because my mother was killed by Russians.

# ACROSS THE BORDER

## *Sabiha Hassan*

I've lived in Bradford for 23 years and brought up my children here. There are so many stories I could tell about how hard it was to make a life in a new country. But instead I'll tell a story that has come down in my family from the time of Partition between India and Pakistan, in 1947 – before I was born.

My family was living in Kashmir, on what is now the Indian side of the border. We had a beautiful house only recently completed. My father was a newspaper publisher and he believed there should be an independent state of Pakistan. He and my uncles wrote about this in the paper. They knew many politicians and powerful people. Some of their friends were Hindu.

My mother says that in our region many people of different religions used to get along very well. Muslims and Hindus shared in each other's festivals and lived as good neighbours. But in 1947 this was becoming much harder.

As Partition came nearer, my father and uncles were in great danger. Our house was near a government guest house where politicians came for holidays. A message came inviting my father to the guest house to see one of his Hindu friends. My uncles were away, and my father knew that in those days even an invitation from a friend might be dangerous.

But he went, and his friend warned him to get across the border before the day of Partition. If my father stayed, assassins would find him. So the whole family left very quickly and quietly, as if on a holiday.

My mother says it never crossed her mind that they wouldn't be coming back. She left her wedding photographs, furniture, everything. She just took the bulbs out of the lights on the porch – a very small precaution. It didn't seem possible that anyone would really want to damage our house.

The journey was very slow, very casual, moving from village to village - just ahead of many stories of destruction. One of my uncles who wasn't married went back secretly to our house – it had been wrecked. But the whole family survived, except one uncle was travelling in India with his bride.

It's horrible to know that he was killed by Muslims. His wife was very beautiful, and the men who caught them on the road thought she was Hindu. People used to think that Hindu women were more beautiful than Muslim women.

They killed my uncle and dragged her away. She sent a message later, but no one could get across the border to help her.

Eventually the family reached the home of another uncle, and started a new life. But so many people will never forget, and long to go back to where they used to live. One aunt who stayed behind used to write to my father, dreaming of the day when she'd see him again. My father was sad that the new border divided Kashmir, and he always hoped for it to be reunited.

# CHILD OF WAR, WOMAN OF PEACE

*Kauser*

Let the child of war
Become the woman of Peace
She knows of war
She has tasted war
She knows what it can do
To families
To children
To individuals
She does not attempt to avoid war
at any cost
She wants to avert it
By negotiating
With people in power.

Let the child of war
Become a pioneer
Become a woman of Peace.

# BULLYING

## *Class 4P*
## Grange Road First School


Hair pulled at the fair.
Pushed off the wall.
Not my fault
Bullies might be there.

In the street,
Stone thrown,
Not my fault,
Bullies might be there.

Bag nicked
on the way to school.
Not my fault,
Bullies might be there.

Pushed off the swing in the park.
Not happy times.
Bullies might be there.

# REMEMBERING GREENHAM

## *Carol Rank*

We have only begun to know the power that lies in us if we
would join our solitudes in the communion of struggle. So
much is unfolding that must complete the gesture, so much is in
bud.

Denise Levertov, from Beginners

Greenham Common, December 1985. I had just come to Bradford from
Berkeley, California, to be part of the University Peace Studies Department for
a while. I wasn't to know then that my life would change, that I would move
here and make my home here. Some of what pulled and kept me here was what
I experienced in those early days.

We had all heard of the Greenham women. The women's peace camp at the
Greenham Common Air Force base near Newbury, Berkshire had existed for
over four years. Through harsh winter weather and the harassment of the
authorities, women had camped outside the base which was occupied by the
United States Air Force as a site for nuclear missiles. Around the world, we
had seen the image of those brave women dancing on the missile silos, affirm-
ing life in the midst of death. On the fourth anniversary of the ringing of the
base, I went down to Greenham with thousands of other women, to join hands
and surround the base in protest against the Cruise missiles there, the weapons
of death, each hundreds of times more destructive than the bombs dropped on
Hiroshima and Nagasaki.

There was mud, mud, everywhere, and chain link fences, and barbed wire
and look-out towers reminding me of the Berlin Wall, where green uniformed
soldiers, all very young, kept watch. The women said that only the Americans
were allowed in the innermost sanctum, with orders to shoot if intruders made
it through to the last barrier. British soldiers could not be trusted to fire on their
own people, especially if those people were women. On the fence were all the
decorations put there by the women – ribbons, photographs of children and

families, teddy bears, poems, and spider webs made of string, representing the webs that weave us together.

Late in the afternoon we attempted to ring the base, turning our backs to the fence, facing outwards as if by forming a human chain, we could send a current through our bodies powerful and positive enough to overcome the terrible destructiveness of that place. As if we could cast a magic spell and make those weapons disappear. It was impossible to know how long the chain of women was. The perimeter was nine miles, with different gates named after the colours of the rainbow. Women old and young were holding hands. A cry went up somewhere far down the line and moved like a wave to us, then through us, and back. A haunting sound, it was repeated again and again, sometimes sounding like a cheer, sometimes a warning, sometimes a taunt, as women were being carried off in police vans for having cut the fence.

As night began to fall, I walked round the fence to another gate and saw tapestries women had sewn, a baby bonnet a grandmother had tied to the fence, and next to these, photographs of the weapons convoys. On the other side of the fence were the young soldiers, trying to appear as if they were ignoring the women, or making sarcastic comments. When one woman began pushing the fence back and forth to prevent the soldiers from repairing a hole the women had cut, several of the men began kicking viciously at her until she let go. One of the soldiers, a baby-faced boy, slouched manfully by the fence, a parody of John Wayne or Rambo or Clint Eastwood. "You don't know what kind of men you're talking to," he drawled. I almost laughed. Could he not see the deadly game of machismo he was playing inside his barbed-wire prison?

Most chilling was to see those man-made mounds of earth covering the missile silos and to know what lay inside. Soldiers patrolled with attack dogs, and searchlights glinted off the wire fence. Was this the green and gentle England I had always heard of? Inside the fence was a realm of death, so ugly and stark, a dark and twisted landscape of a destroyed world. Outside the fence was the realm of life, the common and the women holding candles and singing quiet songs, songs of peace for Christmas, and women's songs, "strong like a mountain". Before the sun went down, I saw a flock of geese fly over the missile silos, messengers from nature, winging their beauty over what humankind, in its stupidity, had created.

That night, around a campfire, a large crowd of us stood in a ring and joined in singing. At the centre of the circle, children toddled about and played as if in a protective embrace. It was a celebration, women came with flutes, tambourines, saxophones, and trumpets, there was dancing and laughter and talking. Women joined arms and moved in concentric circles, spiralling outward, some carrying large candles on stakes as if we were all a part of an ancient ceremony. Flickering lamplights were set aloft on the wind in tissue paper shades. They floated mysteriously up and away into the darkness, adding to the sense of sacredness. It reminded me of a Hiroshima commemoration I was once part of, when we set candles adrift on a stream, each in memory of a lost soul. Next to me, a woman began to cry and so did I.

"Which side are you on?" the women sang. Setting those lights aloft into the night sky, the message seemed to be: free the soul, free the spirit. Come with us out of the world of death. Let us have life.

# PEACE MARCH AMERICA

## Patricia Flynn

In 1986, The International Year of Peace, I had the amazing experience of taking part in a Peace March for Global Nuclear Disarmament in America. The organisers "Pro Peace" had visualized thousands of people of all ages and backgrounds walking, talking and camping their way across middle America for peace.

On March 1st in Los Angeles, California 1,200 marchers, myself included, were given a tremendous send off by thousands of people who lined the streets to offer us their support. Unfortunately only two weeks later, as we walked into Barstow, California, "Pro Peace" declared itself bankrupt. For a few days chaos and despair ensued with vehicles being repossessed and marchers going home. And then as the news spread support of every kind came flooding in, including donations of food and vehicles which enabled approximately 500 of us to continue on the journey for peace.

This was a peace march which would cover 3,700 miles and take nine months to complete ending in Washington D.C. on November 15th. It included crossing a desert, climbing the rockies and walking through cities and countryside as we journeyed across thirteen different states.

We became a moving village as we crossed the country walking between 15 and 20 miles per day and camping somewhere different every night. We all had to contribute in a variety of ways to enable that village to work, the trucks to move, the food to be prepared, the loading and unloading of equipment and the security of each new campsite. We had to cooperate with each other to make decisions and to deal with the group dynamics. We were invited onto radio and TV shows, to church groups, schools and women's groups. We joined local vigils and demos thereby adding our support to local peace initiatives.

We were given incredible support and hospitality throughout the journey by the majority of American people. They prepared food for our arrival and invited us to stay in their homes. On many occasions our numbers swelled as people travelled out to walk with us into their own villages, towns or cities. Friendships between many different kinds of people, young and old were formed in the shared belief in the need for nuclear disarmament. Many of these people were among the 20,000 who joined us in our final demonstration in Washington D.C. on November 15th 1986.

Peace March rests on the Mojave Desert, California

# PEACE

### Scott Robinson
### Ley Top First School

Peace is everywhere
Peace is in the air
Peace is in everyone and everything
So why I want to know why
do people still fight and kill?

# FRIENDS
# AND
# NEIGHBOURS

# NAMES

*Asma Khan*
Waverley Middle School


Listen up come here.
Now let me ask a question.
You don't want to spend your whole life being a colour.
You label yourself
Hindu, Christian, Jew
But that doesn't mean it has to work against you.
The basic fact of the story is,
Where you are, that's where your place is.
The thing I need to emphasise is that it is your
Space.

This is why we must not pollute it -
So next time you finish your crisp packet
Think about where it should go,
On the floor, or in the bin,
Be you black, white or green
The rule we all must obey is to keep the world
CLEAN!

# THE YOUNG STRANGER

*from Melkon's Story, the autobiography of*
*Melkon Guzelian*
*translated from Armenian by Mavis Guzelian*

Look at a map of Turkey and below and to the east of the Taurus Mountains you will see Iskenderun. (The 'finger' of Cyprus points at it). During the time of this story, that is from the end of the First World War in 1914 – when Turkey was defeated – and up to 1938, Iskenderun was part of Syria under French mandate.

The historic Kingdom of Armenia comprised parts of Russia and Turkey. In 1915 the first 'ethnic cleansing' of this century took place, directed against Armenians. Kurdish people never had a nation and the Turkish government used Kurds to attack Armenians, leading to decades of enmity.

When the Armenians of Iskenderun, Antioch and other parts of Cilicia were driven from their homes in 1915 they were directed towards Aleppo, from where many of them were pushed into the desert. They went by two different routes. Some passed through Azaz by way of Kilis before going on to Aleppo; others came through Haman in the direction of Afrine where they crossed the river, then followed the same road to the city.

To the left of the Haman to Afrine road lay an elevated chain of hills known as the Kurt Dagh, or Kurdish mountains, from which Kurds descended on many of the helpless Armenian wayfarers and robbed them before retreating to their villages. Some of those that were robbed came from Soghukoluk, but our group had turned away to Damascus before going far along the Afrine road.

In post-war years a few Kurds came across from the Kurdish Mountains in summer to graze their flocks of goats in the richer pastures of Kizil Dagh. They would bring their produce into our village shops and sell milk from door to door to holiday-makers, since Soghukoluk by then had become a favourite summer resort. Wealthy people from Aleppo and Iskenderun, from as far away as Beirut and Damascus, brought their families here, and many local people let houses to them for the season. We would let two of our houses in the village, but not the house in the khan as we sometimes stayed in it ourselves, though most of the summer we spent at Guzeli.

One summer day my mother was alone in the house in the khan. My father had gone to Aleppo the day before and was not due back until evening. Busy about something as she always was, my mother chanced to look out of the window. Her story of what happened next she would often tell us in later years, though at the time it seemed to have little significance.

My mother saw through the window a strange young man sit shivering in the corner of the khan. She asked Multezim, the farrier who worked there, who he might be, as he seemed to be ill, but Multezim could only tell her that he thought the man was a Kurd. My mother asked the man himself if he were ill. "I've got malaria," he answered her in Turkish. She took him into the house, spread out a mattress and quilt for him and made him some tea, which he drank gratefully before crawling into bed.

She knew that Manushagian, the pharmacist from Iskenderun, would be in the village that day, he was often there in the summer. Up at our coffee house she found someone to take a message to ask him to come, and he soon appeared with his little bag. My mother knew him well. He was a brother of the

Guzelian Family Group – 1929
Melkon, aged 2, second row right with Father and Mother

57

dentist who had a garden at Armutjikh, and of the American citizen Hagop-jan Efendi to whom my family owed so much.

The pharmacist examined the sick man, then gave my mother some medicine for him with instructions as to how often he must take it. "I'll come and see him again," he said as he went.

My father returned from Aleppo and my mother told him about the unknown young man who lay ill in bed in the next room. She gave him a light meal and another dose of medicine before he went to sleep, and in the morning the fever was gone, although he was still very weak. They learnt that he was one of the Kurdish goat herds, and that his name was Abdo.

Next day Abdo's brother came looking for him. Abdo's donkey was still tied up in the khan according to the strict rule in the village forbidding animals to be left in the street. The man recognised the donkey as soon as he saw it and asked the farrier if he had seen its owner, who was his brother.

"Yes," answered Multezim, "he's in that house. He was ill, so they took him in and the doctor came. There," he went on as the pharmacist appeared at that moment, "the man you see there is the doctor. It looks as if he's come again to see your brother."

So pharmacist Manushagian and Heusun, Abdo's younger brother, went into the house together, where they found my parents sitting and talking to the sick man as he lay in bed. The pharmacist saw that the medicine was working well, but he said that it had to be taken regularly for a further week. Abdo stayed in our house till he was well again, then he asked my parents how much he should pay them. My father would not hear of it. "You have been our guest," he said, "We will not speak of money." And they sent him on his way with their blessing.

That year the Kurdish herdsmen remained in the vicinity for another month before driving their goats back towards their own mountains, and very soon the whole incident was forgotten. It was a busy time in Soghukoluk, what with the work in the vineyards and in the gardens, they had no thought for anything else.

Summer passed and it was autumn. The grape season came and went and it was winter. Two of the three winter months the men spent in the mountains hunting wild boar; for my mother there was the perpetual round of work in the house. With winter finally over, spring came and again it was summer. Again Sohukoluk was full of holiday-makers running away from the heat of Aleppo and Iskenderun.

A man whom my parents did not know stopped by our house with two laden donkeys and began to unload them. There were two 20-litre tins of olive oil, a tin of cheese and a sackful of fresh olives newly picked from the tree.

"What's all this?" my mother asked.

"This is a present, for you," the man said. "Don't you recognise me?" It was Abdo the Kurd.

"But we must pay you for all this," my father said.

"That will not do, my friend," Abdo said, "- it's a present I've brought you."

It was the beginning of a friendship between my parents and the five Kurdish brothers, Abdo, Heusun, Hanan, Menan and Muhammed, as well as the husbands of their two sisters, who had mixed all their flocks together and were coming regularly to Soghukoluk each year. After that, every time they came they would bring us tins of olive oil. Sometimes they brought to Guzeli their surplus milk which had remained unsold, again refusing payment. My mother made the milk into yoghurt, straining it through muslin and cooking it in a pan with added salt until it thickened. She would pack it into large glass jars, topping them with olive oil to seal them and keep out the mould.

I first remember Abdo and his brothers when I was four years old and he said to me as they were leaving, "When I come again next year I'll bring you a baby donkey." One of his donkeys was expecting a foal and the very next year, to my delight, he kept his promise.

# COMPROMISE

### *Rashid Javed*
Whetley Middle School

It was July and I was enjoying my summer holidays. I had finished my home-work and could be free. One summer afternoon me and my friend went to the park to enjoy ourselves. We played football and bought each other ice-creams to eat. Then we got bored and wanted a turn on the swings, but there was only one swing available which meant that one of us would be left out. We started arguing about who should have it and soon we broke up. I thought to myself, What have I done? We were good friends and always helped, trusted and cared for each other until now. We stood there looking at each other as someone else took the swing. Soon we knew what we did wrong, so why not be friends again. From that day on we haven't done anything that would upset us.

A famous poet once wrote a beautiful poem. The last verse went something like this:

"Almighty powerful God gives light to a bird to seek its way to God, as a sincere friend."

# IS INTER-RACIAL LOVE JUST FOR FOOLS?

*Michael Woodward*

What will the family say?
"Well at least he isn't gay"
What will the neighbours think?
"She's brown instead of pink"

But look a little closer ...

We've heard about these people
Over-running our land
Milking our welfare system
It's getting out of hand
Let's stick to segregation
Let's seek to stay apart
Smile at them politely
But don't involve the heart

Does God select a favourite shade
And reject all the rest?
Does God approve of mix-and-match
Or are matching colours best?
Can I love this woman
Or am I breaking rules?
Should I look but never touch?
Is inter-racial love just for fools?

# WE CAME TO SCHOOL AS PARROTS

## *Maisie McCabe and Sameera Nawaz*

SAMEERA: I was seven years old when I got friends with Maisie. I saw her playing in the street with some other girls and went up to ask her about Westbourne School. I used to go to Miriam Lord, and Westbourne was newly built then.

MAISIE: I used to go to St Paul's before Westbourne. It was exciting to be in a brand new school. We played rounders, tig, a game called Three Rosies (like the Four Marys in the comic Bunty), and had relay races at the bottom of the playground.

SAMEERA: I was nervous at first but it was really good there. We were in the same group and we used to work together and help each other. Maisie helped me with maths.

MAISIE: Sameera helped me with some spelling. We're at different schools now. I'm at Heaton and Sameera's at Drummond but we still help each other, like with the SATS (Standard Attainment Tests). We both like school.

SAMEERA: We like the same things, that's why we're friends. We both liked reading the Baby-sitter Club books. There was a book week at Westbourne and we decided to sew feathers onto t-shirts and leggings and go to school as parrots. We were first going to come as ducklings, but parrots are more colourful. It took two nights to cut out and sew on the feathers.

MAISIE: We did it at Sameera's house and her sister helped us. We're both okay at sewing.

SAMEERA: My Mum makes clothes for me and my sisters.

MAISIE: Sameera's Mum made me outfits too, a girlie white dress with puffy sleeves and a red velvet dress with white lace.

SAMEERA: We like to play board games – Monopoly, Ludo and Trivial Pursuits, sometimes our sisters join in.

MAISIE: We used to play at being at boarding school, and we acted out ghost stories in fancy dress. At Sameera's house we pretended to be on Blind Date, standing on the window sill behind the curtains answering questions.

SAMEERA: We did have fall outs. Some friends of mine used to try and come between us. In the playground or in the street, friends of mine didn't like Maisie and they used to say, Come and play with us, and I wanted to play with Maisie and they used to drag me away.

MAISIE: Westbourne is mainly Asian children and I felt a bit left out sometimes. Some of Sameera's friends would be against me, but then my friends used to tell Sameera that I was talking about her when I wasn't. I think they were jealous of us. Sameera had an argument with one girl and she started being nice to me and my friend Jessie. When Sameera went home at dinner time she got called names behind her back, but I stuck up for her. A friend of Sameera's used to tease me and call me names.

SAMEERA: Once when a game with water balloons was going on in the street, the others wouldn't let Maisie join in. We went to the shop to buy our own balloons.

Sameera Nawaz and Maisie McCabe

MAISIE: Then they said, "You're copying us!" I sometimes got left out in choosing games. And if there were arguments Sameera sometimes felt she had to take her cousins' side. That was hard. The biggest fall out was when we were playing rounders, on opposite teams. Some girls were saying that it was better in Pakistan and an older girl said, "Why don't you go back there then?" Someone told Sameera I'd said it, which I hadn't and never would.

SAMEERA: That was our biggest fall out. We didn't speak for a week after that. But then Maisie's Mum came across to see my Mum and we got friends again. I think if you're friends you should just ignore what other people say.

MAISIE: You shouldn't let other people stop you being friends. We're alike, that's why we get on.

SAMEERA: What am I looking forward to? My birthday. I'll be 12 on 26th October.

MAISIE: Me too. I'll be 12 on 31st October.

Interview at Westbourne First School, Thursday 17 October 1996

# MY FRIEND JOEL

## Aweis Ben Asghar

Ever since I and Joel were younger my mum and Joel's mum already knew each other, we practically lived next door – though my family's moved now. So when they were friends me and Joel were about four years old and ever since we have really become closer, as in friends, which is really cool. Now that we are older we get to see each other more, such as Sundays when we play basketball at Nab Wood Sports Centre. We do a lot of things together when possible, even though Joel is a year younger and is not at my school.

I have to say that life for me and Joel has not always been perfect. We have pathetic quarrelling. The one I can think of was on Joel's birthday, about four years ago. (He was born on 13 August 1983, or 1981 if he is going to the cinema). The quarrel was because my team won his team and I kept going on about it.

Joel's mum's Jewish which makes him Jewish but it doesn't really mean anything to him – except that his grandparents expect him to go to the synagogue when he stays with them.

Joel is at Nab Wood Grammar School. He's mad on drama, drama and drama and wants to be an actor. He also plays drums.

There are fights in his playground, often about race. Joel says Asians lads go round Bradford in gangs looking tough. I said because people are in a group it doesn't mean they're a gang.

Joel is a very neat friend and I cherish the day we met. I am glad we have stayed friends as good friends are very hard to find. I do realise that a lot of my other friends I have lost due to me moving schools but I hope we can stick to being good chums when we are older.

He complains I never phone him but he is never home so isn't there to know when I do phone.

# AWEIS MI PAL

## Joel Moss

I think Aweis is kinda cool. We met when we were three or four years old. We do a lot of stuff together, like football and basketball and we have a lot in common. We both like pizza (just plain old cheese 'n' tomato). Aweis is allergic to Marmite, which he discovered when he had it at my house.

We've only ever had one real argument but that's a long time ago. He was really annoying me. His mum was really angry because I bent his fingers back

Joel Moss and Aweis Ben Asghar

and then our mums fell out about us, and we were friends and they were still arguing, but then they were friends again.

Aweis goes to Dixon Technology College – doing GCSEs. He feels there's a lot of pressure of life and it was easier to be a little kid. You've got to get GCSEs, A levels, then go to university, then get married and then you work and work and then when you retire nobody likes old people.

Aweis goes to the mosque twice a week and twice a week a mosque teacher comes to his house. He doesn't find it hard to fast in winter, like this year, but some years he has to get up at 2 in the morning and the fast ends at 9 at night and then it's harder.

We both think Bradford's getting really bad – on every corner someone's smoking or doing drugs, not to mention the place is boring and dangerous and small.

Aweis was born on 11 August, 1982, or 1981 if he is going to the cinema. He likes Michael Jackson.

I always seem to be ringing him and he never seems to ring me, but I'm still his mate.

# A VILLAGE IN CONFLICT

## Ivy Wood

In the mid seventies the villagers of Denholme were devastated by an unexpected bombshell. The then Urban District Council unveiled plans for central re-development on a large scale. In three phases the very core of our beloved village was to be completely demolished.

Compulsory purchase orders were issued to house owners in the phase one area, and the limit set for the strong objections which vigorously followed.

Irate villagers gathered, petitions were collected street by street, county councillors were approached and the MP pledged his support. United we were determined to beat the council responsible for this betrayal and who were now declining to attend our meetings, naturally unwilling to face a lynch mob whose cries included, "Sold down the river," and "Fetch back t'stocks".

The council remained adamant, this decision, they insisted, must be adhered to, no more arguments. "Get 'em down, move 'em out," was their attitude.

Forced into acceptance of a disgracefully low price for the homes many had cherished, the first batch of victims were shunted out to be re-housed.

"From back to back to under and over, what's the difference?" some questioned sadly.

Demolition gangs moved in, some of us were reduced to tears, we would sadly miss our old neighbours, the friendship and the cups of tea.

After weeks of noise and clouds of choking dust we faced an open area of grim depression.

"Where there's muck there's money," someone reminded, but it was not for the deprived villagers.

When winter arrived the derelict site assumed a new sinister atmosphere. It was the time of the murderer Peter Sutcliffe's reign of terror and we women were uneasy in the dark because of the proximity of the black wasteland. Again we cursed those responsible for our unhappy situation.

Meanwhile those of us in phase two continued to live with some trepidation, we viewed our future with considerable apprehension. Suddenly things swayed into our favour, there were financial problems and sweeping changes in local government.

The new Bradford Metropolitan Council decided to abandon future demolition and sent out letters confirming the decision. We were jubilant, we were ecstatic, unbelievably we had won, and we didn't care how.

Now we could paint and garden, maintain our property without fear, the old council were redundant and serve them right. Even when the Lord Mayor opened the new complex in 1982 we were still resentful and did not forget our departed friends, particularly when we learnt the new homes would be let on a points system to "Offcomed uns".

We were not prepared for an influx of strangers, suspicious we decided caution was the best policy.

The summer of '83 brought everybody outdoors and the thaw began, gradually we warmed to our new neighbours, the chatting returned and so did the cups of tea.

Ivy Wood making tea at the local bowls pavilion

Twenty years on it is difficult to imagine the outlook as it used to be. Some of the old neighbours have come full circle and now live within the complex just yards away from their old homes. Bitterness has long since disappeared but we who lived through the traumatic years will never forget the events that almost brought a once peaceful village to its knees.

# RANI AND ME

## Bibi Mehrun Nissah

"Why d'ya talk to Hindus?" shouted Shaheen as she pushed me from behind.

I didn't reply to her question. I just walked on down the second-year corridor, pretending I didn't hear her.

"You shouldn't be friends with them!" she shrieked.

I was used to her haughty voice, every time I heard it I felt like melting through the floor.

"Leave me alone," I said wearily. I was tired of her pesky remarks.

"Bibi is a Hindu, Bibi is a Hindu!" She sang this sentence over and over again until she disappeared round the corner.

Shaheen teased me because my best friend was a Hindu and Shaheen didn't like her.

Rano Ram was a very special friend. We went to Whetley First School together, then we came to Whetley Middle.

Rano had long black hair, a round, fair face and brown eyes. She liked to be called Rani.

Me and Rani sometimes played hopscotch on the faded paint markings on the tarmac ground, or we told ghost stories and wandered in other magical worlds. When the hand bell rang for lunch we would charge to the canteen and carry out the ritual of asking what we each had in our lunch boxes. Shaheen made another unexpected and unwanted appearance.

"I din' know you eat pork, Youk! You really are a Hindu!" said Shaheen leaning arrogantly on our table.

"Get lost Shaheen!" shouted Rani.

Shaheen did go away but her terrible song rang in my ears.

Confused thoughts began to haunt me. "Am I a Hindu? Is Shaheen right? Maybe if you play with Hindus, you become one. I don't want to break up with Rani. She's my best friend."

For once I didn't stop on the way home to look at the goats that grazed in the Bradford City Farm field. Streets that told a story every time I walked through them were silent that day.

"Asalamualaykum!" called a cheerful voice from my living room.

Much to my surprise it was my grandfather. I ran to leap into his arms and the cold, dispiriting feelings soon vanished.

"So when didya come?" I asked eagerly.

"A short time ago, and please speak Urdu," replied my grandfather as he gently nipped my cheek with his rough fingers.

The sweet aroma of rice and chicken curry followed Mum into the room as she brought tea and biscuits for us. After a few words she returned to the kitchen, closing the door behind her.

My grandfather soon realised that something was troubling me. After a while of non-stop questioning, I told him the whole story.

"So I'm not a Hindu am I? Will I have to break up wi' Rani?" I asked, searching for an answer in my grandfather's wrinkled face.

"You are a Muslimah because you read the Kalima and you promise to follow the rules of Islam. You can play with anyone you want, you will always be a Muslimah," my grandfather explained. "Here, I will tell you a true story," he said.

"Now long ago, before the division of India, we lived in a village called Ghurgushti, where people of all religions lived together and helped each other. The dusty streets were always safe and calm and the crowded market place was like a friendship fair. In those days I was very poor. I had to find some way to earn money but I did not know what to do. At that time there was a very kind man called Gurditta who was a tailor, and the very best too. He offered to teach me how to sew clothes. I willingly accepted and I began to sew in the little hut which we used as a workshop. The walls of the hut were cracked and rain poured through the roof, but it had to do. It was not long before the whole village praised my work. Gurditta was also very pleased with my work and I was grateful for his help.

We worked together for many years. We celebrated Eid and Diwali together. We were like brothers. Then in 1947 war broke out and soon India was divided into two parts, India and Pakistan. It was a time of great confusion. Muslims and Hindus began to kill each other. Soon the fighting came to our village and ruined the unity there too. Finally the Hindus and Sikhs left the village and fled to India. Gurditta also left. The sad thing was that I was not able to thank him or say farewell. After that I never saw him again. I don't even know whether he survived his journey." Granddad sighed, there was a long silence.

"That was a nice story Baray Abbu," I said as I rested my head on my grandfather's shoulder.

"Now you listen! If you have a special friend do not look at her colour or her religion. Just remember that friendship is special. If anyone teases you then say to them that we must respect everybody... Do not lose your friends, do you understand?" said Granddad in a very strong voice.

"Yes, Baray Abbu ... Thank you ... Shukreeyah!" I said happily.

After that talk, I realised how important friendship is and I learnt to ignore Shaheen's persistent remarks.

Me and Rani went to school together until Third Year, when Dad bought a new house which meant I had to join another school, leaving my best friend behind.

My last day was very emotional. The moment that I had been running away from caught up with me. There Rani stood with tears desperately trying to cling to the rims of her eyes. I slowly walked forward. My heart felt as if it was stuck in my throat and I could feel a warm tear roll down my cheek. Rani handed me her bracelet without saying a word.

My arms helplessly enveloped her and we both silently cried.

"I can't say goodbye ... I'll seeya ... soon," said Rani in a sob and we parted and went our separate ways home.

My pillow was wet that night. I held tightly the bracelet Rani had given to me. Then on the 4th of January we moved into our new home.

A few months passed. I had settled down in my new home and school. One day I decided to visit Rani at school. We were thrilled to see each other again but time passed like the breeze, unnoticed, and soon it was time for me to leave.

"Oh, do you have to go?" Rani moaned, grabbing my sleeve.

"Yeah. I'll come again," I replied, not wanting to leave her.

The same year I went to see Rani on her birthday. Within a few moments she somehow managed to break a chair. It was funny but I can remember her saying, "Do you have to go .. I'm gonna get in big trouble."

After that I never saw her again. My life grew busy. I met new friends. Even today I remember her face and the way she smiled.

The differences in our beliefs made me realise that we can all live together in peace. We don't have to make our past an excuse for feuds today. The unfortunate thing is that I, too, like my grandfather, let go of my best friend. But no matter how far I go I will always treasure the memories of the years we spent together.

# MR ROSE MY NEIGHBOUR FOR 27 YEARS

## *Stephen Walsh*

When you have a neighbour
You can call a friend
Always pleased to give a hand
As through life you wend

Then he is more than neighbour
He is part of you,
Helping one another,
Each day through and through.

I had such a neighbour
As our good Lord knows.
I never had a better friend
Than my neighbour Leslie Rose.

Our Lord has said it's time to go.
His life comes to its end.
Grant him, Lord, eternal peace,
My neighbour and my friend.

God bless.

# STRUGGLING
# THROUGH

# REBEL REBEL

## *Martina Geraldine Gallagher*

I didn't speak out about being bullied until it was happening to my nephew and niece. Then I told them my experiences hoping this would help them to be strong.

It was because of Idi Amin of Uganda that I went to Harpenden, Hertfordshire to the Physically Handicapped School. Idi Amin expelled Asians from Uganda and one of the children he expelled took the place I'd expected to get at Lister Lane School. I was pretty sick about that. I went to Harpenden when I was seven, in 1966, and I stayed there till I was sixteen, coming home only for holidays. I was there through the height of the troubles in Ireland and so met prejudice because of my Irish name. I got blamed for the bombings, though some of my own family were killed. My mother is from Sligo and my father is from Derry. I've met every prejudice there is and I've dished some out too. I was born in Bradford, but I'm Irish.

My mother took the drug Thalidomide and that's the background to my disability. I was born without arms and legs. That drug was manufactured in Germany and so I was deeply prejudiced against Germans. We had a German staff helper, a house mother, at the school in Harpenden, on an exchange. I was really cruel to her – I can see that looking back – but it was my way of handling what was going on around me. I wouldn't let her touch me or come near me.

At the Physically Handicapped School in Harpenden we were isolated and protected. It was extremely regimented which didn't suit me because I've always been a rebel. They don't ask you when you're a child and when you're disabled what your opinion is and I wasn't asked whether I wanted to go into a mainstream secondary school for a couple of days a week between the ages of thirteen and sixteen, like some guinea pig. I was just sent. Nobody asked me how I was getting on either and when I told the head some of the things that happened to me he didn't believe me because he wouldn't accept that the girls whose dads he played golf with could do such horrendous things.

I was bullied for being disabled, bullied for having a different accent, bullied for being Irish. I ignored the verbal bullying and laughed it off. I knew my parents had had to put up with a lot. When they first came to Bradford people in the street used to write Get Out Irish Pigs and leave human excrement. I was brought up not to like English people and Protestants. But none of that prepared me for the bullying I got at school.

I was called Barrel, Tiny Tim, Short Arse, Bionic Woman and obscene names, Fat Bastard, and told that my mother was a dope carrier. I was called Weebel and they'd shout that weebels wobble but they don't fall down. That

Tina Gallagher and a friend

was because sometimes I found it easier to move around on the floor, roll around on the floor. Then they'd try to kick me. If somebody lifts me up, I can't do anything - so they'd do that too. I have small feet and they'd pick me up by my feet and put my head down the loo and flush it and leave me on the floor to crawl back. The teacher never asked, Why is your head wet?

I used to wear artificial legs and I got pushed over. I was tied to a goal post and had to crawl to the classroom on my back across gravel. I used to wear artificial arms that were worked by a special gas and they used to let the gas out. I stopped wearing them. I had a wheelchair that was like a little space ship and they used to tip it up.

I had two friends at the Handicapped School, one Irish and one black girl who had been adopted by a rich couple and came as a day pupil. Kate, my friend who was black, had a liver or kidney problem that meant the whites of her eyes were yellow. She was taunted and other kids would say she'd been put in the oven too long.

If I can, I get my own back. My legs were metal and one girl broke two toes kicking me. Another girl I tripped, accidentally on purpose. I took some trays out of the oven and asked this girl to help me and she burnt her fingers.

When I came back to Bradford from Harpenden, then I was got at for talking like a southerner and people would try and get me to say bath and laugh. I ended up going to elocution lessons to learn to talk Yorkshire again. I was supposed to do 'O' levels at a college in Pudsey but I was semi-literate and had limited maths. There was no support and the teacher was in something like the National Front and didn't hide it. Me and two Asian guys got the lowest marks and a hard time. I reported the teacher.

I went to DATA to learn computers at Broomfield house and there I was a student rep and on the management committee, though none of our recommendations led to anything. I was there for four years and that gave me some confidence.

At a Bradford & Ilkley Community College exhibition I met Brian Franks and he gave me an English assessment. He used to work in the Sue Carol Centre. I did English GCSE and got C and I did maths in the Workshop. I get really bad tempered and impatient but I've had a lot of encouragement from Brian and from Lizzie Lockhart and Margaret Andrew. Margaret's straight, if your work's crap she tells you and she tells you you can do it. I had a black tutor too who did lots of black poetry and stories with us. I liked that. I started the Certificate for Mature Students but I'm taking some time off at the moment. I wanted to prove myself but I over-proved myself and got a bad virus two years ago. I was falling asleep in lectures. Then I started with arthritis and rheumatism. It's when I get a pain in my back and can't walk around that I really miss my legs.

If you're building a Peace Museum – or anything – make sure it's accessible. Borrow a wheel chair, sit in it and see if you can reach what you have to reach.

My family are great. My niece Jessie, she's thirteen and she helps in ways that not all girls her age would, bringing me to the toilet and shower. She makes my tea. She's great.

What's my philosophy? Don't look at someone and judge them on how they look. It's who they are inside that counts. Everyone's got something to offer and we've all got a disability if we acknowledge it. If people don't like me for who I am, it's hard luck for them.

# VIOLATION OF HUMAN RIGHTS

## *Mohinder Singh Chana*

The life in Uganda was good, but we worked hard for it. My father had established his own engineering business and he hoped that his four sons would take over and expand it further. He influenced us to follow careers in engineering and sent me and my brother, as private students, to study mechanical engineering in the U.K. After completing my studies I joined the family business. However, the upheaval in Uganda that occurred in 1972 changed everything for my family and myself.

Asians in Uganda contributed a great deal to the economy, even dominated it, and that created resentment – although the typical pattern of society that often prevailed in the British colonies whereby very little social intermingling between the races – in this case Asians, Europeans and Africans - used to take place, was beginning to crack.

My wife and I were just back from our honeymoon in Kenya when an edict was issued by the dictator, Idi Amin, ordering all Asians to leave the country within 90 days. Life under his government had already become insecure, but we did not expect him to take this action.

One of the most alarming and disconcerting instances used to be when one would come across a roadblock manned by armed and often drunken soldiers, who would harass people - not only Asians but also Africans and Europeans. Their behaviour was very unpredictable and they were often illiterate recruits from Idi Amin's tribe. They would demand to examine an Asian's passport and would find out by the picture which was the right way up to hold it!

We had to leave everything behind except what one could pack in a suitcase! One thing that my father was determined to carry with him, no matter if he could not bring anything else, was the copy of the Sikh scriptures Siri Guru Granth Sahib Ji which has been in our family since the early fifties. We weren't allowed to bring any money (Ugandan shillings had little value anyway!) as our accounts were blocked and transferred to the Bank of Uganda.

In a situation like this, certain issues suddenly dawn on oneself which under normal circumstances seem incidental .... who was going to look after our two dogs? Fortunately we had a European missionary friend who was attached to a Christian mission near Jinja. My father asked him to take all our household goods for the mission and in turn, would he look after the dogs – which he was pleased to do. Some household furniture was given to our servants.

All this process was particularly painful to my father, who had through sheer hard work established his business. Being British citizens, we of course came to Britain. At the airport, while leaving Uganda, my wife's personal jewellery was taken away, and she was only allowed one ring.

In one way we were refugees, but almost all Ugandan Asians paid their own airfares to go to whatever country they were allowed to. Some were helped by the United Nations. On arriving in England, we stayed with relatives in Coventry for a short while. On visiting a relative in Bradford, my father discovered that the houses were cheaper compared to the Midlands or the south and it was also fairly easy to get employment in engineering (in those days). Hence I ended up in Bradford for which a great fondness has developed.

Displaced people in many other parts of the world have suffered far worse than we did. We were fortunate to be able to re-establish ourselves and quickly contribute to where we settled in the new country. I particularly felt very sorry for the very many Africans who could not go anywhere, and suffered under the brutal tyranny of Amin. At least my family and I got out without loss of life and limb. I feel that violations of human rights is one of the most detestable crimes that is committed by tyrannical regimes and active steps should be taken to correct such practices – in order to give peace a chance.

# ON THE BUS

## Olive Bailey

I had this job and I stood at the table near the window and I said to the foreman, "Can I go to the table over there?"

He asked why. I said, "Because my neck feels stiff and in pain from the draught."

He said, "Oh no."

I asked, "Why?" and he said, "Because those people don't want you looking at them down there."

And I said, "Why not, I'm not a monkey. I can look at them and they will look at me."

I went downstairs and told my sister.

She said, "You didn't hear him right."

I said, "Yes I heard him."

Next morning I said to the foreman, "I went to the Advice Bureau and they said to me I must come back to you and hear what you say." (I didn't go the Advice Bureau, I didn't go anywhere, I just said it.)

And he said, "What did I say? I didn't say it. You can get any table you want."

I said, "I don't want any table."

He said, "Any time you have problem come to me."

I said, "My problem is black problem and I won't come back to you any more."

They gave me the bad jobs.

If these things were taken up before something would be done. Now it's too late.

On the bus coming up Leeds Road somebody said, "Where you from, you have no right on this bus, get off," and I said to him, "Where are you from?"

He said, "I am a British subject."

I said, "I am a British subject."

He said, "Were you born here?" and I said, "No, but I have a British passport."

He said, "I can represent this country."

I said, "Well you can't represent your country because now you're drunk." I said, "I can represent my country, Jamaica, but you can't represent here."

And the conductor stopped the bus and did want to put him off but I just said, "Let him go on. I forgive him."

# STRIKE OR SURRENDER
A short story

## *Razia Khan*

The overcast sky burst and rain splattered furiously against the window panes of every home in the country. The cold autumn wind roared with such immense force that every house shook. Far in the distance, a stray dog howled.

Mike snuggled deep down in his bed, wrapping the covers tightly around his large muscular frame. He consulted his watch and realised with shock that it was 11 am yet he was reluctant to get up. For one thing it was absolutely freezing even though last night's outrageous storm had abated, and for another he didn't feel ready to face the outside world.

He gazed around his room aimlessly but the room and its shabby furniture offered no diversion. No matter how hard he tried, Mike failed to block out yesterday evening's horrific and humiliating incident. The memory filled him with feelings of nausea. He felt raw and empty. Deep down inside he yearned for something he couldn't name. Time is supposed to be a healer, yet nine years had failed to heal the emotional scars. Mike had ben disowned and was forced to leave home at the age of fourteen. He learnt to cope with the dangers of the outside world, leading a rough life, trying to make life unbearable for others because deep down he felt betrayed and bitter. Yesterday he had learnt that the callousness and pain he inflicted upon others had done nothing to ease his own distress.

Sighing deeply, he leaned against his pillow and began reflecting upon himself and his past.

He was leader of the Strikers. He didn't remember forming a gang, it was one of those things that just happened. However, he did recall why he behaved in such a brutal manner. After being imprisoned for shop-lifting at his job as an assistant to an Asian employer, Mike had vowed to take revenge. Glen, Jim, Darren and Lee – his gang mates – had fully encouraged him and offered their support.

This thirst for bitter revenge was like a drug which seemed to intoxicate Mike. He'd lost count of the number of people they'd attacked. Glen had called it, Paki bashing, simply because all their victims were Asian. Whether they were innocent or not, to Mike everyone was a culprit, like Rashid his employer.

He recalled how the Strikers had almost beaten one Asian youth to death for no apparent reason. The brutal attack inflicted upon Abdul two weeks ago had made headlines. His attackers were still unknown. Scarred for life, Abdul lay in a coma. Mike winced as he pictured how the victim lay in a pool of blood in an underground subway, where they had left him. He was lucky to have been discovered quickly otherwise Mike was convinced that he would have lost his life.

He recalled further incidents which had ruined several people's lives. Last month Glen and Darren had attacked and burgled a woman in her own home. However, they were caught and were now serving two years in prison cells.

Mike rubbed his bruised jaw and winced with pain; last night's traumatic experience could have resulted in his death. Yet he'd had a narrow escape; fate had spared his life. The lady in black had come to his rescue.

He'd been on his way home from the cinema at 7.30 when his assailants pounced on him. He was dragged into the same subway where Abdul had been attacked. Panic seized him; he automatically reached for the five inch knife tucked away in his boot. But his attackers were far too quick; grabbing his hands they knocked him to the ground, plucking the knife from his boot. A large fist smashed into his face knocking him out completely; his head throbbed like the engine of a helicopter. He felt his heart beating against his chest, causing his blood to pump faster than ever. He tried to open his eyes, but everything seemed blurred; he felt the blood gush out of his nose and spill over his lips. He didn't know how long it was before he regained consciousness. He opened his eyes very slowly, forgetting for an instant where he was. As he drank in the sight of three pairs of legs clad in black designer jeans and boots, reality came flooding back. He allowed his eyes to travel upwards and then halted as they rested upon the faces of his assailants. He stared hard at them, his eyes narrowed to slits as he searched his mind for recognition. No, he was positive he'd never met these Asian youths before, so why had they attacked him? His eyes widened with horror as he saw a knife glinting dangerously in the hands of one of his attackers. The hand controlling the evil looking weapon advanced towards him. "Destroy him!" one of the youth's companions growled. "Let him suffer, and feel the pain he inflicts upon other innocent beings."

From the corner of his eyes, Mike saw something move; he spun his head to look, then wished he hadn't. His jaw dropped open as he gazed with astonishment at the lady before him. Even though he could only see her eyes there was no mistaking who she was. He didn't blame her if she wanted him to suffer. After all, revenge like any other human emotion, is a two-edged sword as dangerous to the person who wields it as the person it is wielded against. Mike was determined to destroy others, but did he really think everyone would allow him to calmly do as he wished. Wouldn't they long to destroy him in return? Tonight he realised just how wrong he was. He recalled how two weeks ago Jim and Lee had callously insulted this lady before she handed over her bag. She had been standing alone one evening at a bus stop when they approached her. She was dressed exactly as she was tonight in a loose ankle-length black robe, and a similar scarf covering her hair and face only revealing her eyes. He remembered how Jim had mocked her, asking her if she'd come from the Arab desert or whether she was a Scottish widow. Lee had referred to her as a black Ninga. She didn't respond but had simply handed over her bag saying, "This is all I have, take it and leave me alone."

They had been shocked by her reaction but had taken the bag and left.

He tore his gaze away as he saw the recognition in her eyes. Mike shuffled uncomfortably. He'd never felt so humiliated in his entire life. Yesterday he'd prowled around like a powerful lion, yet today he lay like a helpless mouse caught by an angry cat.

Face it, he told himself, everything's over. These guys are going to even the score and you'll have to suffer!

As the knife man drew closer, Mike shuddered feeling the hair on his neck rising, a cold chill soared through his body as he pictured death descending upon him. He swallowed hard, tasting his own blood. He felt the urge to throw up. He closed his eyes not wishing to imagine what would come next. Terrified he waited, and for the first time in his life made a silent prayer.

Feeling the cold metal blade tug at his chin he inhaled deeply, fighting for control, and wondered how long his torture would continue.

"No! Don't kill him!" The scream rang out echoing a hundred times, taking everyone by surprise. There was a sudden movement and the lady was standing between the knife and its victim to be. "No!" she cried again. "Leave him, Javed. Spare his life."

"Zara, stay out of this," Javed snapped back. "It's time he was taught a lesson. We'll take his life as a revenge for those who have suffered."

"No," Zara cut in. "What will you achieve? It isn't worth it. He'll soon come to his senses." She turned, giving Mike a cool glance. "What do you get out of it?" she questioned. He looked at her silently then turned away in shame as she continued. "If you are looking for revenge then remember that the Chinese have a famous saying, He who seeks revenge must dig two graves."

Behind her, Javed moved impatiently. "Zara you're wasting time. This is none of your business so stay out of it!"

She glared at him. "Forget it, Javed, look what happened to Abdul. When will you people learn? I swear you'll achieve nothing. Make peace. Let him go, please."

Javed remained obstinate. He'd been waiting for this moment for months. Zara wasn't prepared to give in so easily. She didn't understand why humans turned to violence as a means of solving their problems. Why did they fail to perceive how pointless it was? She was determined to persuade Javed. "Think in the long run," she pleaded. "You're deliberately causing problems for yourself."

Javed refused to budge.

Ten minutes later Mike gazed admiringly at his saviour. Zara had convinced Javed and his two companions that they had made the correct decision. "Just a word of warning," Javed cautioned, as he shoved his knife into his boot. "Any more violent attacks after this and we'll erase you from the face of this earth. We wish to make peace, that means all the Strikers must surrender and fulfil their side of the bargain."

Mike was only too glad to surrender. He inhaled and exhaled several times before he was convinced that he was going to survive. He agreed to peace, thanking Zara with all his heart for having saved his life. He looked at her in wonder and a newly found respect, wishing he could express his gratitude in a better way. She thrust a small card towards him, instructing him to read and think about it carefully.

As they left the subway together, Javed turned to Zara. "I'm glad you came tonight," he said. "You made me see through a different light."

"It's about time you people came to your senses," Zara replied, laughing at Javed's serious expression. She glanced across at Mike, who was listening in silence. He looked at her, wanting to say something. Before they parted, he managed to mumble, "Thanks for your help."

"You're welcome," she returned good naturedly, then continued in a more serious tone. "Tonight you were lucky; if you've any sense you'll learn from this traumatic experience. Life's too short to waste. Turning to violence for any reason is the attitude of a coward. Then she looked at him directly. "You don't strike me as a coward, so why act like one?"

Mike reached under his pillow and brought out the small card she had given him. "Peace-makers," the words stared at him boldly, reminding him of his promise. He read the card curiously and discovered that it was a small organisation on the outskirts of town, designed to make peace amongst people from all races, and help them cross the barriers of their distinct cultures which forced one human apart from another. So Zara was a member of "Peace-makers". No wonder she'd helped him even though she'd been one of his victims. Her words echoed in his mind. "What do you achieve?"

She was right. It was time to put the past behind and begin a better future. It would be a challenge but he was determined to succeed. As all kinds of ideas washed through him, he sprang out of bed, forgetting the cold. He dressed hurriedly, slipped the small card into his pocket and raced out of the house towards "Peace-makers", where he was convinced Zara would be waiting to help him achieve his goal, and accomplish the mission he was about to begin.

# RELUCTANT VOYAGER

## *Muhammed Hussain*

I was born in the village of Thikhrian in the province of Punjab, district Gujerat, in the days before the Partition of India. My father was serving with the British Indian Army, stationed in Hong Kong, and my mother and we children lived with our grandfather, my father's father.

Times were hard for us during and after the Second World War, and we struggled to make a living from the land. We thought our father had been killed in action because we received a letter from the British Government that didn't mention his whereabouts. There was a lot of confusion and uncertainty after the war. Fortunately my father returned safe and well. One day he just walked back into the village and we were so happy to see him.

Because there were no jobs in our area, my father decided to take my older brother and myself to Malaya where there were greater opportunities. My mother strongly opposed this at first as she and my younger brother were to be left behind. But eventually she agreed, and we said goodbye to her.

That year of 1946 was a period of trauma, crisis and lawlessness, with conflict between Hindus and Muslims. There were many lectures, public discussions and rallies about freedom and independence. It was a bad time to set out on a long journey, but that was just what we did. We called at Sialkot, a large town, about 35 miles away, as my father had agreed to escort the wife and son of a friend of his who was already in Malaya. At Sialkot I saw my first radio and was astounded to hear sound coming out of a box.

Our whole party then went on to Lahore and from there to Calcutta where we stayed in a sort of travellers' lodge for Muslims called Serai, built by the Moghuls. I was mesmerised by the sights and sounds of the city – the big river, boats, cars and everything.

Every day my father and his friends went to the shipping office to try to get tickets to Singapore but with no luck. Thirty to forty days passed and each day my father and his friends went to the shipping office, only to hear the same reply: all the ships were fully booked. The novelty of the city wore off and I became homesick and weary of the violence: the rioting, killing, burnings and fires. There was a cobbler who usually worked on the pavement outside our

Serai. One day I saw him murdered. A man just stabbed him in the back and somebody else lifted the lid of the grate and threw the body in. That is what it was like.

But despite my fear, I decided I had to be with my mother. In an instant, without telling my father, I just ran, making for the Howda railway station though I didn't really know what direction I was going. Somehow I got to the station, without money, without anything only what I stood up in. I went just beyond the station to the sidings and waited until it was dark. I hoped to find a way onto the platform, yet was afraid to pass the signal box where two Hindu men worked; I remember that one of them was lame. The men saw me and I was terrified. I thought I was going to be attacked.

One of them beckoned to me and I had no choice but to go towards them. He spoke to me in Bengali, which I didn't understand, and then in Urdu or Hindi. "Who are you? What are you doing here?" he asked.

I started to cry. "My father is taking me to Malaya and I want to go back home to my mother," I said. Fortunately they treated me kindly, gave me food, drink and shelter. Slowly they made me tell the story of where I came from and where I wanted to go back to. Then they warned me against going, telling me that the journey was long, I would be caught, and it was too dangerous. They said that I would be better going with my father to Malaya. But I said that I must go back to my mother.

So they put me on the train that came in at 8 o'clock and was due to leave at 9. One of them gave me a small coin which I put in the drawstring of my trousers. I was in a carriage with Muslims and Pathans and felt safe and happy. Everyone was trying to get on the train that I was on. I stood looking out of the window.

However, by this time I had been missed and my father and his friends searched the city for me. They came to the station in a 'Muslim taxi' (Hindus and Muslims used separate taxis) and started at different ends of the platform, looking for me on the train. My father spotted me and pulled me off. After a few more days we got on a ship for Singapore, and from there to Malaya.

It was five years before I saw my mother again, and I got a hero's welcome when I returned because not many people from our village worked abroad in those days.

# KNOW BETTER, DO BETTER

## Brother Egbert A Wright

One time when I was working, the foreman said to me that I was a monkey. I said to him that I am certainly sure that whatever God made He hasn't made it in one colour so if you look at me, as a black man, and believe I am a monkey then so are you, as a white man, a monkey. After listening and hearing what I had to say we became friends after that. There are people they just pick at you because of your colour but for you who know better, as the Bible says, we should do better.

Brother Egbert A Wright, Federation of Caribbean Elderly

A few months ago I was with a group of people and they were talking about the riots that went on in Manningham last year with Asians and whites and so I said there are two things that cause us to be living how we are at the moment and that is class barrier and colour barrier. Irrespective of how rich you may be and how poor I am, we are all coming from the same place. We are all made by the same Hand. Even though you may be rich, at the end of the day, when my life or yours comes to an end, there are two or three ways of disposing of the body. Some may ask for a watery grave, some for cremation, some to be returned to the earth we came from. Until we know that we are all one human being irrespective of creed, colour, nationality and when we can teach our children this – for many of us have children who were born and grew here - and because they may sit down and listen and hear about the treatment of what took place with their ancestors who were taken from Africa to the West Indies, hatred may grow in their hearts. We can teach in school and at home that we are one in humanity. My parents taught me how to live among people and to help the elders and respect and honour them.

How will things change? The main thing is to educate our children and ourselves. We are never too old to learn. Say to yourselves, These people suffered since they came here and we must try to break down segregation between us as people

# OUR ENVIRONMENT

## *Emma Booth*
## Waverley Middle School

The sea is already polluted.
Some fish are already dead.

Trees are being cut down right to the ground
Animals are being killed.

Pollution is killing our atmousfear
And it's killing us too.

If we don't do something about it, who will?
It's our environment that's being killed.

By our cars
Why should animals suffer
When the pollution is getting tuffer.
It's our mistake.

# HELPING
# HANDS

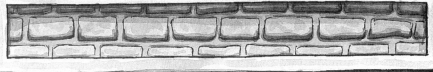

# UNDERSTAND THE JOURNEY WE WERE FORCED TO MAKE

### *Krystyna Naplocha*

I was born in Poland where I led a very happy life until the dreaded September of 1939 when the Second World War broke out. In February of the year 1940, during a very severe winter, there was a knock on the door at 2 a.m. A young Russian soldier told us to get ready to leave.

I will not forget that soldier because he must have known what was going to happen to us. "Take everything," he said and gave us chance to pack. Others were less fortunate.

There were six of us, mother, father and four children. I was twelve years old.

It was a journey to Siberia that was to last three months. I remember it vividly, the cold cattle trucks that were heated only once every twenty four hours by means of an iron stove. We slept in bunks that were constructed to take as many bodies as possible. If you wanted to turn over at night you had to struggle because we slept so close to each other that there was no room for such luxuries as stretching your arms and bending your knees. We had to adapt to these dreadful conditions as we were told umpteen times when we asked for the name of the destination, simply to obey and not to ask questions. Half way through our journey we were taken to a town where we were allowed the luxury of having a shower. There was a special reason for this. Because of the conditions that we were travelling in we soon discovered that we were covered in lice and sores which were getting worse by the day. Our clothes were taken into the de-lousing chamber and we had a shower, a clean towel and a bar of soap.

But soon that was forgotten as we were to spend another six weeks in the grime and smoke resulting from our faulty stove. Our sanitation was an old bucket standing in a secluded spot, partitioned off by a blanket. At that time we were fed once a day on the same kind of cabbage soup brought to us by the guards. We were allowed some bread and boiled water. Once in a while we had some sugar cubes as a treat. People were ill and depressed. Those who had chronic illnesses died and were thrown off the truck as we travelled.

I am pointing this out not to shock you but to give you a picture of the conditions we had to endure. Even today when you meet people from Eastern Europe of the older generation here in Bradford you might wonder why they harbour so much fear and resentment. This is the result of our war time traumas and persecution. Many people suffer nervous breakdowns as a result of these experiences. They do not want to talk of their experiences. Many have psychological disorders and there is no treatment. As they age, the traumas of the war seem to return. For example, if you put certain people into a residential nursing home, they will react in a specific way by saying, "They are putting me into the camps again," the camps being those of the Second World War. They are frightened at the suggestion of a home and do not want to leave the safety of their own house. No matter what conditions these people live in they still want to hang on to their independence. Sometimes it means fighting the authorities, even though as their health deteriorates they know that they cannot succeed. We must therefore look at the needs of these people with compassion and understanding. It is not our fault that my generation had to endure this

At the Polish Centre
Krystyna Naplocha seated, right.

dreadful struggle just to survive. So please remember, when dealing with elderly people of East European origin that they deserve to be treated extra carefully and with great understanding.

Now I would like to come to the present day and outline a few facts about the lives of our people. Through the years we have worked very hard to build up homes and raise our families as well as we could. But always, inevitably, there were thoughts of the relatives left behind who were undergoing hardships. Many of us used to send food parcels regularly. We found strength and compassion by grouping together, particularly around our church which gave us hope and a meaning to life. We tried hard to bring up and educate our children born in this free country. We maintained our traditions, not only those with a religious aspect but also those relating to every day life. Slowly our prosperity grew but we never forgot those days when we were poor and homeless. We never asked for grants or charity as we were not afraid and quite prepared to work hard to achieve what we have now.

The years have flown and now we are retired, but even after living in England for fifty years we still feel that our hearts belong to Poland or whichever country our roots lie in.

Many of us have returned to visit our countries but have found that they have changed a lot and differ greatly from our memories of them. Our way of life in Britain is quite different from theirs and sometimes we wonder if we could adapt to live there again.

You may find strange habits amongst the East European peoples. For example, we believe that to waste food is sinful. This attitude is the result of being in a position of actually being hungry and seeing children die like flies from starvation. This is why many elderly people seem to have large amounts of food stored in their homes. I know that we have not got a food crisis but the older generation wants to be prepared for the worst to come. This is a life long habit and cannot be changed. Also, many people have great difficulty dealing with official papers and the normal everyday mail they receive. We do not understand why, but as the years draw on many people seem to lose their knowledge of the English language and now find themselves cut off from neighbours and unable to communicate their needs. This is the result of fate. So we need more and more help from the younger generation to get us through the hard and lonely years of retirement.

We have Polish Centres in Bradford, one next to our church in Edmund Street and another in Shearbridge Road, for ex-servicemen. These centres are very popular and often visited by our people. But there comes a time when the ill or infirm cannot go out alone so we have to rely on Social Services to help us bring these people together.

We have been very lucky that for three years our premises have been available to the infirm as a result of the funding of transport by the Social Services. These centres are also a meeting point for people who have had to be placed in residential or nursing homes and have no contact with other Polish people. They are seldom happy if they are alone with no other Polish people so we are trying to get them placed together in the company of others of the same nationality, which is good for morale and general well being. Now we have a couple of Polish speaking out-workers who visit people and see to their needs and help where possible. Sometimes the visit in itself is a great event for those living alone – a chance for them to converse.

Very few Polish people complain of being ill-treated or neglected. Those in residential homes are well looked after and are comfortable. Each person is an individual and please always remember the very difficult times these people have lived through and then you will understand them better.

# THE CABINS

## *Bernadette Jarvis*

I've worked here in the Cabins on Canterbury Estate for five years. It's a really positive, happy place, a multi-cultural building where people can feel safe. Loads of things happen here. People come together to make changes, make things happen. It's important to have hope in your life – we survive on memories and so if we provide some good memories for people then we help people to survive.

We have carnivals, open air discos, a float at the Festival, activities around the Duke of Edinburgh Award Scheme, we take people away on trips – all sorts of things. We have study support for kids of an evening, with a teacher. Some children have passed their GCSEs who failed the first time. Kids walk in after school like it's their second home. With the community worker, I developed a programme to keep children safe which involves story and role play. We have all kinds of courses for adults too. Sometimes someone will come in for help filling in a form or something like that, and stay for a course.

Some Asian lasses walk around with a smile on their face and people say,"Aren't they friendly?" but sometimes there's sadness inside and they smile because they don't speak English. Sometimes I'll knock on a door and say to a husband, "Let your wife come to the Cabins," and he'll say, "No, she's not coming." And I'll say, "Why not? Come over yourself and take a look." Then he'll come and take a look, and say, "Oh I suppose it's all right here", and his wife will come over after that. One person who comes here, she could hardly speak English at first and she's now got her City and Guilds in Creche Work and is doing well. We like to see people go on and achieve something after starting out here, and lots do.

# WE REMEMBER THE EARTHQUAKE

## *Kantibhai Panchal*

It was the earthquake of 1993 in India that led to the creation of a day centre for the elderly in the Hindu community.

When we heard of the earthquake we knew we had to do something as so many people were left without family and homes. We started a collection at the supermarkets and around our community. We told people that "Today is their turn, tomorrow might be yours! What will happen to you? What happens to the children? What happens to the family? What happens to the future?"

Those caught in the earthquake would need to be fed tomorrow as well as today, they would need a new home.

Three persons travelled by British Airways to India so that they could see that the money collected was distributed fairly. Our community in Bradford was brought together by the suffering of those in the earthquake and as we helped re-build their community we found an energy within our own to bring people together. We decided to do something on a permanent basis. There was no day centre for Hindus, so now once a week the elderly of our community come together.

Our aim is to get people out of the house, to come under one roof and to be one community regardless of colour, race or anything ... we don't follow the caste system here.

The elderly do not speak English and are fearful to go out but here they can all come together and learn about England. We teach them how to look after themselves and we share our problems.

We remember the earthquake and the need to help other people. This Sunday we are all going to donate blood so we can help others.

This summer the Hindu marathon is in Bradford. There will be 10,000 people as the Hindu community comes together in peace and unity. There will be a small fun run which the elderly can walk around.

At the day centre we always sing and pray for unity and for peace in the world.

# STAND YOUR GROUND

*Max Prosper of the West Indian Parents' Association*
*talks to Frances McNeil*

Max Prosper came to England when he was 19 years old, to a very different England where people complained if you played your radiogram on Sunday. Max smiles as he remembers, "Now it is English people who make the noise."

"We were a curiosity," Max says. "They had heard of black people or seen pictures but never seen us with the naked eye."

Max is from Dominica in the Windward Islands. When I met him he was trying to find time in his busy schedule to teach a class in Patois at the West Indian Parents' Association where he is Centre Administrator.

This seems a fitting post because education has always been important to Max. When he filled in his reason for coming to England on his passport application, he wrote "to further my education". Coming to England was the expected thing in those days and when, for the umpteenth time, he heard the words, "Are you still here? I thought you would've gone to England long ago," Max packed his bags.

First Max went to Bristol, then came to Bradford, "following the crowd". Bradford was a good place to be for a young man who wanted to improve his education. Courses at Bradford Technical College were well publicised and Max attended college part-time in the evenings.

From 1956 to 1964 he worked on the buses, first as a conductor with a regular route between Bradford Moor and Saltaire and later as a driver. His depot was at Ludlum Street off Manchester Road. One night he was walking home alone when five teddy boys crossed from the other side of the road to Max's side and walked threateningly towards him, their hands touching so that Max would be unable to pass. Max did not hesitate. "I will die, but one of you will go with me," he said. "Which one of you will it be?"

None of them wanted to die. Max went on his way.

Another incident occurred on the last bus from Bolton Junction to Bankfoot. A group of lads got on and when Max went up, saying "Fares Please," he was pushed from one youth to the other as each said another would pay. Max stopped the bus. "You will pay or I'll call the police," he said. The other passengers joined in, saying to the lads, "You're holding up the bus". The young men paid.

Max gained his Ordinary National Certificate in Engineering and worked for a number of companies, including International Harvesters. Unfortunately, redundancy became all too familiar, but one constant in Max's life was the voluntary work he did in his spare time.

Max's own children have succeeded in the education system, achieving an impressive array of qualifications and posts including honours degrees, masters degrees and a professorship in Physics at a university in Florida. One son is a freelance artist.

Other children were not so fortunate. "Some 18 years back our children were being sent to schools for the educationally sub-normal," Max said. "Especially children who were brought here having started their schooling in the

Max Prosper, West Indian Parents' Association

Caribbean. We didn't understand the system here. At home you'd meet your child's teacher in the street or in the shop or going to church and they'd say, Oh your child needs extra tuition. Here you get set phrases from the teacher and it doesn't have anything to do with your child at all."

A group of parents, including Deloris Daniel as secretary and Max as treasurer, decided to form the West Indian Parents' Association. Much impetus came from John Samuels, Tutor for West Indian Youth employed by the then Bradford College.

With a grant from the Commission for Racial Equality, they started a Saturday supplementary school in premises on Manville Terrace provided by the college. A day nursery followed and a music programme. There is also a lunch club for the black elderly which meets twice a week, although they would like to extend this.

There have been success stories among the children who have attended the supplementary classes, and among former employees and members who have gone on to successful careers. In his review of the first ten years of the West Indian Parents' Association, John Samuels wrote, "much has been achieved but there is still much work to be done".

Max Prosper and his dedicated colleagues and co-workers still stand their ground.

The greatest revenge is to live well.

# THE TEDDY BEAR

## *Joy Atherton*

I work for Bradford Nightstop which provides emergency accommodation for young homeless people in the homes of volunteers. Many people arrive with little, but one young woman came with five bin bags which were left in the office while she stayed on Nightstop.

At the end of her stay, she dipped into one of her bags and gave us a teddy bear that she'd made herself, in Leeds United colours. A few weeks later, she sent this poem.

Joy Atherton, Bradford Nightstop

# Being Homeless

Life can be a downer
whoever you are,
but being homeless
leaves so many scars.

No money, no home,
no future ahead.
Where can we go,
we don't even have a bed.

No money for food,
or even a cuppa,
so we stay cold
and sing for our supper.

A shop doorway,
or a cardboard box,
even a wet bench,
that's our lot.

Nothing to look forward to,
no future ahead.
Just carry on
until something is said.

# DON'T WEARY IN WELL DOING

## Nathaniel Johnson

When I come to Bradford, looking for a room I'd see a sign, Room to Let. Knock on the door. They'd see my black face and say, "It's taken".

You know the only way we get room, it was through the Polish and the Indians. The English wouldn't give us a room.

One day at the bus stop a little girl come up to me.

"Hello, mister, can you show me your tail? My mama said black man have tail."

"Go tell your mum, whenever I can see her tail, I'll show you mine."

I retire 1980, I took my pocket-book and go to the people I know retire, take their name and address and go to this meeting, workshop they call it, at

At the Federation of Caribbean Elderly, Gulberg Centre

Melton House because the Social Services wasn't doing anything like that toward us. It was me alone as coloured man with Asians and Whites. But I am not one who weary in well doing. The time will come when they realise people like us want a place. From there I founded the Federation of Caribbean Elderly. Daphne, Kelly and Hanson came. Our first premises were on Claremont. Lilian Philip went, to a church hall on East Street. I went to the council and said, "What I am doing, you should be doing it." They found us Birchland.

Help came from Val Glenny at Age Concern. She came to see the books I kept and she was impressed. "You do something like this before?" she asked. "These books is in perfect good order."

I got the Telegraph & Argus to come out with a camera to take a picture of the grant that Val Glenny got for us. But anyone who help us, they move them on. One Asian fellow got us furniture for Birchland and they move him on.

All we people who come in the fifties and sixties getting old now and want somewhere to come out of the house. People here they praise and bless and say, "We happy to come out during the day."

# THIS IS NOT ART

## Anne Fabian

Two or three years ago, the Bradford Synagogue walls were daubed with Anti-Semitic signs, using paint. Around this time in sub-ways and on walls along one or two roads, there were slogans of an anti-semitic nature. Some referred to the Holocaust, saying this had never happened. It disappoints me that in a multi-racial community like Bradford, as we approach the twenty first century, there is a minority who have learnt nothing, and who have animosity towards people of other races and religions.

On the opposite side of the road to the Synagogue is an Asian taxi service. The people there informed the anti-graffiti firm in Bradford about the daubings on the walls, then they told the police and then the Chairman of the Synagogue, Mr K Fabian. The graffiti was removed very quickly.

It is encouraging to know there are still decent neighbours, and good people living in Bradford. Following the civil disturbances in the City, I may add, the Bradford Synagogue – along with other places of worship – was not attacked or damaged.

# LIVING IN A WIDER WORLD

## *Balu Lad*

The village where I was born in Gujarat was 50-50 Hindus and Muslims, sharing all the special times, and taking sweets to each other's homes. We were poor and my father went to Uganda to earn money. When I was ten, I went to join him. I had my first pair of shoes for that trip. I had my first pair of long trousers when I was nineteen.

Balu Lad, centre, with fellow students

In our village in Uganda, Muslims, Sikhs, Hindus lived together with Buddhists, Jains and Christians. These were all people who had left family behind in India and come to earn a living. I qualified as a teacher and taught in the village. I was invited to all the religious and social functions of the families of my pupils and I got more and more into charity work, St John Ambulance and so on.

When Idi Amin came to power, we knew politically that things would be difficult, though I'm not sure that we expected the expulsion of Asians. Being a teacher and a British passport holder, I came here. I lodged with friends in Leicester but my qualifications were not recognised. With only £10 in my pocket after the journey, I did whatever jobs I could get.

I had an auntie in Bradford and moved here when I was offered a job with a bit more money. I started attending evening classes. After I got married there was more encouragement to move forward and I qualified as a radio and TV engineer. Having started in Africa as a teacher, I wanted to return to the profession I loved. I took a further evening course and gained a post graduate certificate in education.

I also got more into community work and continued with the St John Ambulance, Laisterdyke branch. After the Thornton Lane mandir was opened and the deities were installed, I became involved there. For the last 17 years I've taught Gujarati as mother tongue to children and young people at the mandir, on a voluntary basis.

As secretary of the mandir I got involved in building bridges between communities. We welcome people to visit the mandir and share our festivities and our beliefs. The temple and the community centre has become a focus for studying and learning about Hinduism and the Hindu community living in Bradford.

I've been through the stages of poverty and I don't want others to go through them. With that reason I do as much as I can to help others to improve their education or give them necessary advice and help. I spend most of my spare time in social work.

# DO YOU REALLY KNOW WHAT JEWISH PEOPLE ARE LIKE?

*Nora Hirschel*

Although my parents came from Switzerland, I was born – actually in Manningham – and bred in Bradford, where I've lived all my life and been a member of the Reform Synagogue, now an Honorary Life President.

One of my closest friends has many Jewish friends. Years ago, one of her friends was asked to give a talk about Judaism at the Aldersgate Methodist Church. He didn't really want to do it, and the invitation got passed on to her. She didn't want to do it either, so she asked me.

That was the first time that I did a talk, but soon afterwards a friend who was a Commissioner in the Guides asked me to do another – I've been involved with Guiding for a long time. She had a Ranger company (now called a unit) and one of them was a probationer at Bradford Royal Infirmary. A Jewish patient had died, and the hospital staff had not been allowed to lay out the body, because there was a Jewish group with particular responsibility for that task.

The probationer had a very strange idea about the bodies of Jewish people being stood up in this process of preparation for burial. I'd never heard of such a thing, but discovered later that it was a common misconception among Gentiles. My friend the Commissioner asked me to come and talk to the company about Judaism to sort out the confusion.

After that, more and more people began asking me to talk to all sorts of groups. I was a member of the first consultative committee about religious education in Bradford, before the Interfaith Education Centre was set up. I've had experience as a teacher and I enjoy visiting schools to help with religious education. But it's best when groups of children or adults can visit the synagogue.

When adult groups come, I often ask them, "If you met me on the street in Bradford, would you think that I was Jewish?" They laugh or look confused, and say no. There are stereotypes about the way Jewish people look - long nose, black curly hair, dripping with jewelry. I don't fit that mental picture of a

Jewess, and it's good for visitors to a synagogue to think about their own misconceptions.

Interfaith work has become very important to me over the past fifteen to twenty years, just as the synagogue was so important to my father. I shall keep up this work as long as I live.

# OLIVE OIL ON PRESCRIPTION

## *Silvana Hanson talks to Stan Brooksbank*

Silvana enjoys meeting people. Now partly retired, she works for the Oxfam shop in Duckworth Lane and helps in the cafe at Lynfield Mount Hospital. She remembers her early days in Bradford, just after the Second World War, very vividly.

"Every week me and my friend Libera used to go shopping to Bradford market greengrocers and come home with two rabbits and vegetables. There was rationing and my mother-in-law said, 'How do you get this food and you can't even speak English?' I didn't tell her the man on the stall had been a soldier in Italy." Silvana Hanson laughs at the memory. It was the 1940s and Bradford was a dreary but friendly place for Silvana. Besides, she and Fred were together and that was good enough.

She was born Silvana Giovannoni, in 1922 in Florence, Italy. Her family had commercial, scientific and literary connections. Her father, Alfredo, a socialist and anti-fascist, died when she was two years old and her mother was left to raise Silvana and her two sisters. Silvana's mother worked as an upholsterer in a furniture store and later Silvana acquired her mother's skill with a needle.

Silvana left school and obtained work making shirts at a factory in the port of Genoa, living with relations. Genoa was bombed in the early days of the war and Silvana returned to Florence, thinking that if she was going to be killed it would be better to be with her family. She recalls one particular event when an Italian partisan shot a German soldier and the Germans took revenge by demolishing a street of houses, setting mines in every house. The priest went to complain and was told that the only reason reprisals hadn't been taken in Italian lives was because the German soldier was known to be a looter and a thief.

As the war dragged on, food became more and more scarce. The bread ration was 200 grammes a day. "My sister was feeding her husband because he was working and she died, aged only 30, of under-nourishment and lack of medical attention," Silvana remembers sadly, showing me a family photograph. When the British arrived at the River Arno the bridges had been destroyed and some hungry people swam the river to get food.

Although the Italians capitulated in September, 1943, it was not until the end of 1944 that the Germans were driven out of Florence. That was when Fred Hanson, aged 24, a soldier in the Royal Army Service Corps, came into her life. The British had opened a bakery in an old chocolate factory close to Silvana's home. Fred worked at the bakery, from which bread was sent to the Salvation Army who delivered it to the British forces. They got to know one another and met often at the local picture house.

They decided to marry, but had to wait six months for Fred to obtain permission. The wedding was at the Sacra Familia Church in Florence on 9 March 1946. Fred was transferred to Trieste and Silvana went there to meet him, hitching, walking and even sleeping out in the grass one night on the way. Only later did she realise the dangers of her journey.

There was little work available in Italy and they decided to come to Fred's home in Bradford. A lot of Italians came to Shipley to find work in the mills. A number of Italian girls married Polish men at the end of the war.

Silvana went to a transit camp in Austria then travelled to England via Germany. Arriving at night at a black, smoky Victoria Station in London was like arriving in hell. With two friends, she managed to find somewhere to stay the night. In Florence the shops had been open late and one friend thought it would be the same here and wanted to buy false eyelashes. She was out of luck.

In Bradford the buildings were dark and depressing and the food bland. Silvana's doctor took pity on her and gave her prescriptions to get olive oil, which all Italians use for cooking and which in England was then available only through a chemist. Silvana and Fred lived with Fred's mother in Oakenshaw. Silvana had packed a trunk containing her trousseau of fine china and a silk nightie but it never arrived. Her compensation took the form of a few extra coupons with which they bought a table, four chairs and a rag rug.

Fred's mother baked cakes and Fred and his brother went round with a horse and cart selling them. When Silvana went into hospital to have her baby, another young woman asked if she'd had the extra eggs pregnant women were entitled to. Silvana hadn't had them: her mother-in-law used them for baking.

Silvana and Fred have three daughters and a son. In Florence the schools were spotless and so were the children. Children put their hands on the desk each morning and any children who failed the clean fingernail test were sent to the toilet to have their nails scrubbed. St Williams School on Ingleby Road was a shock to Silvana and she disliked seeing her children going into such a dirty place with an outside toilet.

It was in 1956 that Silvana and Fred bought a baker's shop in Duckworth Lane. Fred's experience in the army and later at Clarke's bakery in Oak Lane gave him the necessary knowledge to start his own business. Silvana helped in the bakehouse and served in the shop.

In March 1996 Silvana and Fred went to a surprise party at the Bankfield Hotel, Cottingley. Their four children, twelve grandchildren and two great grandchildren were there to celebrate Silvana and Fred's Golden Wedding Anniversary.

# THE PEACE
# INSIDE

# PEACE

*Shaun Chapman*
Ley Top First School

Peaceful is
working in a group
hearing quiet music
playing games
being warmth, reading in bed
in a cinema

Unpeaceful is
hearing the toilet flush
shouting in markets
in a football ground
crunching polystyrene

# FRIENDSHIP

*Anon*

What is the meaning of friendship? Friends are those people who share your problems, your bad times, or your good times. The truth is that my best friends are my books. When I feel lonely or upset, my books make me happy. When I read a similar story to my own experience, then I think, If this character can bear it, why not me? So at this time I feel much satisfaction.

My favourite books are about famous people. I like writers who try to write bravely and truthfully. Sometimes the truth is very sad. Each true story shows you a pure emotion - the essence of life.

# EVERY SCAR MEANS A LESSON LEARNT

## *Faiz A Nasir*

Life itself is a collection of stories and instances of bashes and blushes and scars of experience. When I came to this country from the Gulf, I had been working as a stores supervisor in Qatar. When you arrived in the UK you had to go to the Labour Exchange and tell them what work you could do. I told the man at the Bradford Exchange that I was a storekeeper, and he wrote down "unskilled textile worker".

"That isn't right," I said to him, "I am a storekeeper."

He went and spoke to another official. The other man waved him away and said, "It doesn't matter, don't change what you've put." Unskilled labour was all they wanted us for.

I accepted that, in order to get a job and save money for my family to join me from Pakistan. Over the years I have faced many hard decisions – to stand up for my rights or to move on in life – to distinguish where the duty lies.

I was given a card to report at 6 p.m. the same day to Baildon Combing Company in Shipley. The overlooker for the night shift was a very kind, elderly gentleman. He was not happy to employ me for the job and its prospects after realising that I have some education. But that was the only work available for me.

The job was wool-pulling, pushing huge blocks of very dirty, filthy-smelling wool into the washing plant. The work required me to move piles of wool continuously from 7 p.m. to 7 a.m. with a break of 15-20 minutes about midnight for some food.

That was the first night of my work in England – the end of a dream held from my school days that there is something called "dignity of Labour" in England. I was given a blue overall to put on as mill soldier's uniform.

When break time came I was almost exhausted and lost. But a young man attracted me with gentle, sympathetic gestures. He operated combing machines and introduced himself as Ker Singh from Fiji. Ker Singh offered me very genuinely to share with him food he had brought for himself.

Faiz Nasir and Ker Singh

That was the start of a peaceful, loving friendship between us. As long as I worked in the Baildon mill we both brought our separate food packs but ate jointly, sharing in all aspects of our social life over the years. Our families became friends to each other. Life dragged us in different directions but we never separated our hearts.

We very rarely see each other in these old-aged days. But in our hearts and minds we are at peace and feel comfortable about each other, that we have great regard for each other as human beings.

The song of an Indian film Ker Singh used to sing to me in 1962 still echoes in my mind. "Na Hindoo benega, Na Musalman benega. Tu Insan ki oulaad hai Insan hee benega." A mother sings to her baby in the film: "You will not be Hindu, neither will you be Muslim. You are the child of a human being and you will grow as a human being yourself."

# STILL TRAVELLING ON

## Tara Mistry

*"There is only one religion, the religion of love. There is only
one caste, the caste of humanity. There is only one language, the
language of the heart. There is only one God, He is
Omnipresent." (Guru Sri Sathya Sai Baba, South India)*

When it rains here in Bradford and the grass has that particular scent of both
freshness and decay, I remember the rainy season in Gujarat, the smell of mud
and earth. As a child, I helped to protect my grandmother's crops of wheat, bar-
ley and rice by acting as a bird scarer.

In Bradford at Diwali, we make coloured patterns with chalk. In Gujarat,
Diwali's harvest link is stronger. The astonishingly intricate Rangoli patterns
that make everyone feel welcome are made with coloured powder and created
at night, by lamplight, on the last day of Diwali - a beautiful and exciting time.
I would love to go back for a year and learn that skill again. When you work
outside, you feel the oneness of the world.

I was born in Mombasa, but when I was 7 or 8 we went to spend a year with
my grandmother in Gujarat. My grandfather had died and she was living alone,
managing the house and land. She had done that through most of their married
life, while he worked in Kenya. Later, my father sent my mother and us children to Gujarat again when the situation in Kenya was not so good any more.

My father went to England to work, first sending for my eldest brother and
then the rest of the family when he had bought a house. My sister was used to
going without shoes in the warm weather and she was barefoot when we
stepped off the plane into the cold at Heathrow. One of the stewardesses carried her across to the airport building.

With so many upheavals, I wasn't able to do 'O' levels at school in Rugby.
I worked for Barclaycard and then Prudential. When it was time to think about
getting married, I said that I didn't want to marry anyone from Bradford – it
was too cold, damp and horrible!

But of all the young men I was introduced to, the one I liked came from Bradford. We got married, and lived with his brothers at first. Then we bought a house of our own and started our family. My husband was doing further study in optometry, so I took an evening job at Grattan. We didn't feel the hardship – it seemed to bring us closer.

We'll stay in Bradford now, with my husband's business and my work at the Interfaith Education Centre. We lived in Halifax for a year, and Kanti tried working in Coventry, but we always come back to Bradford. Diwali commemorates the return of Rama to his own Kingdom of Ayodhya after an exile of fourteen years. Perhaps Bradford is our Ayodhya.

My guru's mission is to unite people of different faiths and help to create a peaceful world. I'm happy here in Bradford, where my husband's business is and my work at the Interfaith Education Centre. Still, I wouldn't mind going round the world some day – to visit places of pilgrimage of different faiths. I'm always willing to learn from all sorts of people.

# A DAY IN MY LIFE

## *Anon*

I was gone nineteen years old at the time and working in an hotel in Cumbria. One morning my older sister Susan phoned me and through tears told me my mum was dead. Only a few weeks earlier my mum had been up to Cumbria for the day to visit me on my day off. When she set off home at the end of that day I had an unexplained feeling that I wouldn't see her again. I cried about that at the time and didn't understand it.

When I was told my mum was dead many different thoughts came into my head all in a matter of moments. One of them was maybe Susan was suffering from some sort of mental illness all of a sudden and she wasn't responsible for what she was saying and it wasn't the truth. About an hour later my boss was driving me home down a motorway. He was talking about cricket, obviously not knowing what else to say. He dropped me off at a family friend's house and left straight away.

Susan and her husband Paul were there, and I found out what had happened. My mum had been working at a local working men's club in the evening. It was only two minutes away from our house. The council were building new flats for elderly people and the pathways were very much like the rest of the building site. On her way home that night she must have stumbled on some of the rubble that was about, and fallen over into the road at the very same moment that a young woman was passing on a motorbike coming home from seeing her boyfriend. The result was an accident that left my mum dead.

After many tears and comforts, I said I wanted to go and see the woman who was riding the bike. Everyone seemed alarmed at this. People tried to talk me out of it, even tried to get me to take some of the valiums that a doctor had left for anybody who felt they might need one or two. I didn't want a valium. What a stupid doctor. I knew I needed to go see the woman who I found out was called Helen and she only lived around the corner from where we were.

Susan and Paul came with me. Although they didn't want to go, they didn't want me to go by myself. Perhaps they thought I was going to do something stupid. I don't know what they thought. All I remember about things at this point was I wasn't angry at Helen but I did need to see her. I think I was nervous as we got to the house. I knocked on the door. An older woman answered, her face red and sore looking, like she had been crying forever. This was Helen's mum. Susan and Paul were standing behind me when I asked if I could see Helen. Her mum said we couldn't as something terrible had happened. I told her I know what has happened. I told her I was Patricia Jones' daughter. Helen's mum started crying again, saying she was sorry for what had happened. I didn't want her to feel afraid of me or think I was going to start shouting at her so I said things like, "It's okay. Don't worry. It's not your fault." I hoped to reassure her and I think she then realised there were not going to be any hateful scenes.

I remember Helen's mum telling me she and Helen did want to come around to see my mum's family but they were advised by the police to stay away. She did then invite us into her home, through the front door of her terrace house into the back room where Helen was sitting.

Her mum introduced us to Helen. I don't know what Helen must have thought at that moment – maybe lots of different things. Her face was so red, her eyes were bloodshot and she also looked as if she had been crying forever. Her legs had cuts on them. She was so sorry, she was so upset that my heart went out to her. This sounds really odd, because this woman had just been part of the death of my mum and I loved my mum like any daughter loves her mum, but hating Helen would not change what had happened.

We were invited to sit down. At the back wall of the room was a sideboard, one of those big wooden ones with dining chairs at either end and that was where Susan and Paul sat. (I think the two of them found the whole thing very uncomfortable.) I remember thinking that I hadn't come to sit at the back. I hadn't gone through this much hurt to sit at the back. I went and sat next to Helen. It was so sad. We cried. We talked. She told me she was going to cancel a holiday she had booked with her boyfriend because of what had happened, and already she seemed to me to be thinking she had no right to enjoy her life because my mum was dead and we were suffering as a result. But it wasn't Helen's fault. It was an accident. I didn't want her to think for the rest of her life that someone hated her or blamed her.

I can't recall what was said or done on that day and maybe other people saw things differently, but I did go from Helen's house knowing something had happened that would make my life different from what it would have been if I hadn't seen Helen that day.

I consider myself fortunate to have been able to make my peace with Helen whilst she was still alive. It was hard and a painful thing to go through but I did it and I know without a doubt that God was entwined in that day.

All the names in this story have been changed.

# THE GREENGROCER'S SON

## Dirk Bijl

The greengrocer's son was dressed in immaculate white as for a special occasion. I know now that it was a sign of mourning.

When he saw me getting out of my car, he changed direction and came straight towards me. I could see the beautiful and delicate white embroidery on his upper garment. As soon as he reached me, he offered his hand and solemnly shook mine. He told me that his grandmother had died, how she had finally succumbed to a series of heart attacks, and how his family had buried her.

It was clear that he had loved his grandmother very deeply, although he never used these words. In short, he shared his grief. I was deeply moved and full of wonder that someone who was on the face of it so very different from myself, even distant from me, could break through barriers to share his grief. But how could I express my feelings of caring and compassion in a way which was meaningful to him?

He is a Muslim and my inkling of how much prayer means to devout Muslims gave me the answer to my question. I said to him that I would pray for his grandmother, for him and for his family. He thanked me, solemnly shook my hand again and went on his way.

I told this story to the preacher at our next morning service and the congregation prayed, as I had already prayed alone.

When I met my young friend again and told him of our prayers, he had tears in his eyes.

# JAMES AND THE RATE FIXER

## *Nathaniel Johnson*

I work, I work, I work, I work, I work. I had some arguments. The rate fixer come to give me a rate for the job. I said to the rate fixer, "A man told me about you."

He said, "Which man?"

I said, "James."

I said, "When you go home, take your Bible and read James, Chapter 5. 'Come now, you rich, weep and howl for your misery that shall come upon you. Your riches have rotted and your suit is moth eaten and your gold and silver is canker and the rust will burn your flesh like fire. The wages of the labourers, you kept back by fraud'."

Him foam, him foam I tell you and went away and him come back with a better time for the job. I said, "Did you read that chapter I gave you last night to read?"

Him say, "Aw c'mon."

# THE SMILE

## Edith Steele

A tiny figure, old and bent,
So slowly on the street she went.
Her clothes were poor but neat.
Well worn shoes upon her feet.
With work worn hands her bag she clutched,
At sight of her my heart was touched.
What sort of life was it she led?
Was some one there to see her fed?
These thoughts were in my mind,
As I followed on behind.
Then as I passed, I turned to look
Into her face, my senses shook.
The look of peace and quiet there,
As if her thoughts were turned in prayer.
And then she smiled, oh such a smile,
That showed her life had been worth while.
No earthly riches had she gained,
But she had triumphed o'er life's pain.
As I went on my heart was light,
Warmed by the sight of her sweet smile.

# A SLICE OF SILENCE

## Richard Thompson

We live in an age of distraction! Radio, newspapers, advertisements, colleagues, friends, relatives – all demand our attention.

Background music inside shops and supermarkets takes over from the continuous drone of cars and lorries outside. In the evening, television swallows our attention whole. It is not surprising that we are often fragmented, nervous and tired.

What can we do, other than continually react to these demands like nervous puppets on a string?

It seems to me that our greatest need is occasionally to reach down below these distractions to seek the level where we can begin to see ourselves straight and learn how to respond from our true centre, rather than react. It is here that we become aware of God in our hearts. We can learn, deliberately, to set aside every day a certain period of time to reach for this inner calm. In other words, to take a "slice of silence".

This term, "a slice of silence," originated in my work with youngsters during residential educational courses which I ran a number of years ago. Monday lunch was our first meal together. It was then, when we were all assembled, that I introduced to them the first course of every meal - a slice of silence. I explained that the reason for the slice was to make a break from the business of the morning's activities; to help us realise just where we were and what we were doing; to make us aware of the food before us and our friends next to us, and finally to give silent thanks. There were, inevitably, a few giggles which I allowed to subside and then the short silence of say 30 seconds began.

Soon, the slice of silence before a meal became a habit. It was heartening for me to receive, for example, by Wednesday breakfast, a request from a single table of burly 14-year olds. "Sir, could we have our slice of silence?" Which they did, some closing their eyes, some looking outside, others just sitting. Children appreciated it, and brought their own approach.

I believe there are three requirements for one's daily slice of silence: time, regularity and one's own approach. Just 10 minutes in a morning seems impossible but it can be done. That 10 minutes of inward calm starts us off ready to respond to life's demands from our true centre. Next, regular practice is important.

Athletes know from experience the value of daily training. As it is with the physical, so it is with our spiritual form. Relying on wishful thinking gets us nowhere.

Finally, each one of us has our own way into silence. One person may be helped by a reading of the Holy Scriptures, another by music or by the contemplation of a beautiful object.

Whatever approach you use, you can go back into the world of activity and noise strengthened and made whole by your slice of silence.

# WHAT IS PEACE?

*Afsana Ali*
Frizinghall Middle School

Peace is setting people free
Peace will be the people's victory
Peace is the light of the world.

# Supporting organisations

## The Commonweal Collection

c/o JB Priestley Library
University of Bradford
Bradford West Yorkshire BD7 1DP
Tel: 01274 383404
Fax: 01274 383398
E-mail: commonweal@bradford.ac.uk

The Commonweal Collection is an independent, specialist library, devoted to issues around nonviolent social change. It was established to promote the common good by nonviolent means. Open to the public. Contact the above address for details.

## Interfaith Education Centre

Listerhills Road
Bradford BD7 1HD
Tel: 01274 731674
Fax: 01274 731621
E-mail: interfaith@bradford.gov.uk

The Interfaith Education Centre is a resource centre which supports the implementation of Bradford LEA's Agreed Syllabus for Religious Education, provides training for professional groups in Religious and Cultural Awareness, and encourages close links with the various faith communities in the city and the surrounding area.

## The Peace Museum

Jacob's Well, Manchester Road
Bradford
BD1 5RW
Tel: 01274 754009
Fax: 01274 752618
E-mail: peacemuseum@bradford.gov.uk
Website: http://www.bradford.gov.uk/tourism/museums/peacemuseum.htm

The Peace Museum, an initiative of the Give Peace a Chance Trust, has a growing collection of art and artefacts, films, archives and other material on peace-making, nonviolence, conflict resolution and related themes. The Museum office organises travelling exhibitions, workshops, seminars, film shows and other activities.

### Touchstone Centre
32 Merton Road
Bradford BD7 1RE
Tel: 01274 721626
Fax: 01274 395324

Touchstone is a Methodist Church base for City Centre, Interfaith and Higher Education Chaplaincy work, with a Library, Resources Room and meeting rooms open to all. Touchstone works with many different communities across Bradford to build relationships and encourage shared visions.

### MCB University Press
60/62 Toller Lane
Bradford BD8 9BY
Tel: 01274 777700
Fax: 01274 785200

MCB University Press was founded thirty years ago by a group of academics from the University of Bradford Management Centre to provide consultancy services. It has since evolved into one of the leading specialist academic and professional management publishers in the English-speaking world. MCB employs around 140 staff and is based in Bradford with regional offices in Malaysia, Alabama USA, with representative offices in Australia, Brazil and Argentina.